Weight Loss
for Everyone the
TA Way

OTHER BOOKS BY FRANK J. BRUNO

The Story of Psychology
Think Yourself Thin
Psychology: A Life-Centered Approach
Human Adjustment and Personal Growth: Seven Pathways

Weight Loss for Everyone the TA Way

Frank J. Bruno, Ph.D.

HARPER & ROW, PUBLISHERS

New York, Hagerstown, San Francisco, London

FIRST EDITION

Designed by Stephanie Krasnow

Library of Congress Cataloging in Publication Data
Bruno, Frank Joe, 1930–
  Weight loss for everyone the TA way.
  Bibliography: p.
  Includes index.
  1. Reducing—Psychological aspects. 2. Transactional analysis. I. Title.
RM222.2.B79   1978   616.3′98′0651   77–3740
ISBN 0–06–010529–1

78 79 80 81 10 9 8 7 6 5 4 3 2 1

*For those who seek realistic and effective ways
to be permanently rid of unwanted fat*

Contents

Acknowledgments   xi

Preface   xiii

1:   Transactional Analysis and Weight Control   1

   Truth and Transactional Analysis   2
   What Is Overeating?   3
   Kinds of Hunger   4
   Overview of TA   6
   Attaining a Normal Weight   9

2:   How Your Parent Makes You Fat   10

   The Parent   11
   What Your Parents Said   14
   The Composition of the Parent   17
   What Does Your Parent Say Now?   18
   Diet Is a Four-Letter Word   26
   Contacting Your Parent   27
   Coping with Your Parent   28

3:   How Your Child Makes You Fat   31

   The Child   32
   The Composition of the Child   33

The Little Professor   37
Trading Stamps and Rackets   38
Friends and Your Child   40
Kid Foods   42
Excuses   43
The Child and Magic   45
Contacting Your Child   47
Coping with Your Child   48

4: How the Food Industry Appeals to the Child   52

Magazine Promotion   53
Television Advertising   57
Coffee Shops Sell More Than Coffee   60
Take-Out Chains   62
Wine and Dine   64
Supermarketing in the Supermarkets   65
Breakfast Cereals   69
The Manipulated Person   70
Spell-Breaking in the Twentieth Century   71

5: The Life Positions and the Overweight Person   74

I'm Not OK—You're OK   77
I'm OK—You're Not OK   82
I'm Not OK—You're Not OK   87
I'm OK—You're OK   91
Deciding to Be OK   96

6: Fat-Making Transactions   99

Complementary Transactions   101
Crossed Transactions   106
Ulterior Transactions   108
The Gallows Transaction   111
Freedom from Fat-Making Transactions   114

7: Games Fat People Play   117

    The Players   118
    Why Do People Play Games?   119
    "Compulsive Eater," or "Someone to Watch
        Over Me"   119
    "Fat Recluse," or "I Never Go Anywhere"   122
    "If You Loved Me for Me"   124
    "Fat Clown," or "Watch Me Make a Fool of
        Myself"   126
    "Look How Hard I've Tried to Lose Weight"   127
    "Help Me Lose Weight, Dr. Dodo"   129
    Fat-Making Wooden Legs   131
        "Alice in Fatland"   131
        "Gourmet"   132
        "Dumbo"   133
        "My Destiny"   133
        "Junk Food Junkie"   134
    Ending the Games   135
    Game-Free Living   136

8: Fat-Making Scripts   138

    Of Hexes and Curses   139
    The "Looking for Love Script"   141
    The "Conquest of Fat Mountain"   143
    The "Everybody Look at Me" Script   144
    The "Going Crazy" Script   146
    The Counterscript and the Antiscript   149
    Breaking Free from Scripts   151

9: Using Your Adult to Lose Weight   154

    Insight and Action   155
    Ways of Getting Strokes   156
    Assertive Living and Assertive Eating   159
    Unmaking Fat-Making Habits   162

Freedom from Emotional Slavery 164
Psychological Distance and Field Independence 166
Concentration on Eating 171
Writing Dialogues Between Ego States 172
The Skillful Will 174
An Adult Eating Plan 175
Activating Your Adult 178

10: Freedom from Fat 179

The Parent Protests 179
Childhood's End 180
The Joys of Adulthood 181
Four Stages Toward Liberation 182
A Final Word 184

Glossary 186

Bibliography 191

Index 193

Acknowledgments

A number of people have helped me to make this book become a reality. My gratitude is expressed to:

My overweight clients and students for sharing their inner psychological worlds with me.

My wife, Jeanne, for her support and encouragement.

Irv Levy, director of the Barnes and Noble Division of Harper & Row, for his basic confidence in the book.

Jeanne Flagg, editor of the book, for her many constructive suggestions. Her creative interest in the manuscript greatly improved the finished product.

Pat Moore for typing the manuscript.

Frank J. Bruno

Preface

This book is based on a very simple premise: you are overweight because you overeat. And why do you overeat? If you are like most overweight people, you overeat because you are caught in a maze of fat-making thought, feeling, and behavior patterns. In Transactional Analysis, or TA, these self-defeating patterns are called games, roles, and scripts.

About three years ago I began using TA in my classes in the psychology of weight control. I must admit I was tardy in coming to this. In 1967 I read Eric Berne's *Games People Play,* but completely missed its powerful implications for weight control. However, once I started to use the TA approach in my counseling of overweight people, both individually and in groups, there seemed to be no end to the number of ways TA principles could be applied to their problems. It has been very gratifying to see the great impact that an understanding of TA can have on the overeater.

The value of TA for those of you who are overweight is that it gives you a "handle" on your problem. It makes clear *why* you have developed such self-defeating behavior patterns and why you persist in following them. More than that, it shows you *how* you can break free from these outdated patterns. Thus it offers you real hope of a future in which you will have *attained* and will be able to *maintain* a normal weight.

When I write about overeating, I write not only from my experience as a psychologist, but from firsthand experience. I was fat throughout most of my childhood, adolescence, and early adulthood. In junior high school I weighed 195 pounds, about 60 or 70 pounds too much for my height and frame. At 20 years old I was 245 pounds, my top weight. I went through the usual succession of physicians and "solutions" for my weight problem. I took thyroid pills, pituitary shots, and appetite-depressant pills. I went on all sorts of diets. Nothing worked. When I entered the University of California at Los Angeles (UCLA) in 1950 as a junior, I was still fat. Two years later, at age 21, I had acquired a B.A. degree in psychology and had lost 75 pounds. I was a normal weight for the first time in more than a decade. And I have kept the weight off.

It was then, 25 years ago, that I first conceived of the possibility of using my newly won knowledge of psychology to help persons who are overweight because they overeat. However, I realized that I needed a great deal more education and experience before I could be really effective. I received a doctorate in psychology in 1967 and then began seriously to work with overweight clients in psychotherapy and counseling. Since that time I have worked closely with several hundred persons with weight problems.

In this book I have combined my personal experience, my understanding of general psychology, and my working knowledge of TA principles into a useful amalgam. If your problem is overeating, I believe you will find the book encouraging and helpful. No prior knowledge of TA is assumed, although those of you who have read other books on TA will find that most of the concepts have been put to good use here. All terms are explained as they are introduced, and a glossary is provided for quick reference should this be needed.

Weight Loss
for Everyone the
TA Way

1

Transactional Analysis and Weight Control

What is Transactional Analysis? Transactional Analysis is a systematic study of the way in which people communicate with each other. It is also a study of the way people communicate *within themselves*. Thus it has a good deal to say about thinking, talking, body language, and other forms of personal expression.

What does all this have to do with weight control? Just this: the way you think (talk to yourself in your head) and the way you communicate with other people determine much of your behavior. Eating is behavior, is it not? Therefore there is a direct connection between eating and thinking, talking, communicating. Let's consider an actual example:

Helen G. is a twenty-four-year-old mother of three children. She is well educated, holds a teaching credential, and has read a great deal. She recently read a book by a traditional psychoanalyst, and it convinced her that she is a compulsive eater. When she eats in the afternoon during a bout with boredom, a little voice in her head says, "What else can you expect? You're a compulsive eater."

She is replaying, like a tape recording, the message she acquired from the book, the message suggesting she is a compulsive eater. The "You're a compulsive eater" message has become part of what in TA is called the Parent ego state. For the moment, think of Helen's "Parent" as a kind of inner judge of her behavior.

By listening to replays of this message, Helen is indoctrinating herself and forming an increasingly poor self-image. We have here a case of the self-fulfilling prophecy. "I'm a compulsive eater because I do a great deal of unnecessary eating; I do a great deal of unnecessary eating because I'm a compulsive eater." There's nothing productive about this kind of circular thinking, and Helen's problem is getting worse.

Let's take another example:

Max E. has been married for ten years. He wouldn't admit it in so many words, but he feels that his wife is the top dog in his marriage. She treats him the way an insensitive parent treats a child: puts him down, criticizes him, gives him orders, and often ignores him. Why does he take it? Because he's in what TA would refer to as the I'm not OK—You're OK life position. This is his conclusion about himself, a decision made in his early childhood.

Max is obese and his wife is sleek and slim. It isn't much of a wonder. He eats like a starving man. He *is* starving—starving for a little affection.

Perhaps I have convinced you through these two examples that your eating behavior is directly related to your internal transactions (thinking and talking to yourself) and your external transactions (communication with others). If you have eating problems and a related weight problem, you can profit by learning more about Transactional Analysis and applying what you learn to yourself.

TRUTH AND TRANSACTIONAL ANALYSIS

At this point a reservation should be issued. Some persons are possessed of inordinate zeal, and when they discover a system like TA they latch on to it and it becomes The Truth for them.

Others, disagreeing with this point or that point in the system, reject TA. They are like the proverbial mother who throws out the baby with the bath water.

The fact is, TA is neither The Truth, nor Revelation, nor the final word in psychology. *It is a conceptual system that is useful.* Beyond that, there is no mystery. TA's concepts are presented in easy-to-grasp popular words such as Parent, Child, Adult, stroke, game, and script. These words and the concepts they represent are *tools* by which one can change undesirable emotional reactions and behavior patterns into desirable ones. A grasp of the principles of TA can help you come to grips with self-destructive and self-defeating patterns of eating.

WHAT IS OVEREATING?

What is overeating? The word "overeating" covers a host of eating errors. These are some of the things overeaters do:

1. They develop preferences for high-calorie and/or high-carbohydrate foods. These are frequently foods with high concentrations of white flour, refined sugar, and fat.
2. They take too many helpings at mealtime.
3. They eat too often and too much between meals.
4. They eat the wrong things between meals.
5. They eat more when they are in the presence of others who are eating.
6. They seem to be spellbound by food, are often unable to resist food when it is placed before them.
7. They eat when they are not physically hungry. It seems that even when their stomachs are full they continue to have appetites.
8. They eat rapidly, overindulging before they realize what they have done.
9. They go "on a diet," then "cheat."

This is the general pattern of overeating. You may not do everything on the list. Or you may make eating errors not listed. But whatever poor eating habits you may have, there are practical ways to break free from them.

Of course, overeating is not the only determinant of obesity. I certainly recognize that body type, heredity, the acquisition of excessive fat cells in early childhood, defective carbohydrate metabolism, glandular problems, and central nervous system disorders may play a role in the acquisition of unwanted fat. If you feel that these factors are significant in your case, you should consult a physician.

KINDS OF HUNGER

We all know about physical hunger. It is primarily associated with blood glucose levels. When blood glucose falls below normal, we experience a desire to eat. However, there are other kinds of hunger. Eric Berne, the originator of TA, used the word "hunger" quite frequently in his books. He identified three kinds of psychological hunger: (1) stimulus hunger, (2) structure hunger, and (3) recognition hunger. These three psychological hungers play important roles in overeating, and it is important that we understand their modes of operation.

Stimulus hunger refers to the need for sensory experiences —the need to see things, to hear sounds, to touch objects, to smell various fragrances, and to taste foods. Berne notes that it is the need for stimulation that motivates people to ride roller coasters. It is the same need that makes it so difficult to tolerate solitary confinement. When one is experiencing a stimulus hunger that cannot be readily satisfied through normal channels, it is easy to use food as a substitute. The prisoner in solitary confinement might live for his meals. Less obviously, a person who feels understimulated by his or her life situation might turn to food. For example, an assembly line worker may gorge himself at break time, and a mother of young children, confined to a poorly furnished apartment, might eat throughout the day.

Structure hunger refers to the need to structure time with some kind of purposeful activity. Gratifying and meaningful work is one common way of satisfying structure hunger. This is one reason that many people experience structure hunger on weekends. They are faced with the lack of a purposeful activity. They aren't happy until plans have been made. For example, once we have decided "We're going to go on a picnic today," structure hunger is taken care of. We have to pack the lunch, get the car ready, decide if we can get there in time to get a good spot, call some friends and find out if they want to meet us, and so forth. Now we're busy and there is no more structure hunger.

When people experience structure hunger they are likely to stuff the emptiness with food. For example, Nancy Y's children are away at college and her husband works long hours. She does not work, has no hobbies, takes no classes, and has few friends. She overeats simply because it is something to do. It is one of the ways she deals with her structure hunger.

Recognition hunger refers to the need for affection in the broadest sense of the word. It is the desire to be noticed, attended to, and—of course—loved. In TA terminology, *strokes* are the experiences that satisfy recognition hunger. When another person speaks to you, compliments you, gives you positive attention, you are being stroked. It is also possible to get negative strokes. You may get criticized, insulted, and put down. It appears that our recognition hunger is so great that if we can't figure out any way to get positive strokes, we will opt for negative strokes.

Some people build up a large and chronic stroke hunger. They are simply not getting enough attention, affection, or love. For these individuals, food may become a stand-in for what is absent in reality. Thus eating is a way of stroking oneself. It isn't a very satisfying way. It's a fattening way. But it briefly reduces the pain of a chronic stroke hunger.

All the psychological hungers cited play a role in overeating.

But the most important one is recognition hunger, a hunger for strokes. Learning how to obtain positive strokes and avoid negative ones is an important part of using TA to control weight.

OVERVIEW OF TA

Because this book assumes no prior knowledge of TA, I am presenting here a brief overview to establish a frame of reference. The overview is general in nature, and makes no attempt to relate TA theory to weight control. If you are already conversant with TA, you can safely skip this section.

TA can be broken down into five different kinds of analysis. These are: (1) structural analysis, (2) existential analysis, (3) transactional analysis proper, (4) game analysis, and (5) script analysis. Let's examine each of these kinds of analysis.

Structural analysis. Structural analysis is TA's contribution to individual psychology and the study of personality. As the term implies, it is concerned with the analysis of the personality structure. TA sees the personality as being made up of *ego states,* conscious states of mind, mood, and behavior. The three principal ego states are the Parent, the Child, and the Adult (see Figure 1). They are capitalized to distinguish them from actual parents, children, and adults. The Parent ego state is active when you think, feel, and behave in ways you remember your actual parent or another authority figure acted during your childhood. The Child ego state is active when you think, feel, and behave in ways you acted as an actual child. The Adult ego state is active when you are thinking for yourself in a realistic, objective, and responsible manner. The aim of structural analysis is to put the Adult in charge of a person's life.

Existential analysis. Existential analysis is the analysis of what TA calls *life positions,* conscious stances we take toward existence. In the most general sense, these positions can be thought of as upbeat or downbeat. Persons with upbeat positions think well of themselves and like other people. Persons

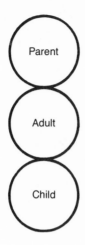

Figure 1. Structural diagram of the personality.

with downbeat positions think poorly of themselves and tend to distrust other people. The aim of existential analysis is to help a person consciously adopt what is known in TA as the I'm OK —You're OK position, an upbeat position in which the individual sees himself or herself as OK (has high self-esteem) and simultaneously sees others as OK (has high positive regard for people in general).

Transactional analysis proper. Transactional analysis proper is the analysis of the gives and takes between people. Any kind of personal exchange between people is defined as a transaction. A transaction requires (1) at least two persons, (2) a transactional stimulus, and (3) a transactional response. Let's say that Joe sees Harry walking toward him in a hallway where they work. Joe raises his hand in greeting and says, "Hi, Harry." This is the transactional stimulus. Harry returns the salutation with a "Good morning, Joe." This is the transactional response. The give and take itself is the *transaction,* the unit of social intercourse. The exchange between Harry and Joe was an example of a pleasant and innocuous transaction. It is clear, however, that transactions can be either constructive or destructive. They can serve to enhance relationships or to alienate people from each other. The aim of Transactional Analysis is to foster constructive transactions that enhance relationships.

Game analysis. Game analysis is the analysis of chains of transactions proceeding to predictable outcomes. As conceived in TA, games usually involve manipulation, double-dealing, and insincerity. Their purpose is not to have fun, but to use and even abuse others for selfish aims. Thus a TA game is serious business, and tends to have long-run destructive effects on human relationships. People tend to play games out of Parent ego states, Child ego states, and downbeat life positions. The aim of game analysis is to free the individual from the tyranny of games so that he or she can attain authentic relationships with other persons.

Script analysis. Script analysis is the analysis of unconscious life plans. TA asserts that most of us make a decision in childhood from the Child ego state to follow a certain course in life. This course is fundamentally either negative or positive. If negative, the person is known as a loser. Such persons set themselves up for failure. If positive, the person is known as a winner. Such persons accomplish their goals in life. The aim of script analysis is to help persons who have decided to be losers to reevaluate their early decision, to *redecide* that they have the potentialities to become winners.

In sum, the five kinds of analysis described above are designed to help people help themselves to lead more rewarding lives. TA usually summarizes the idea of a rewarding life under two general capacities: the capacity for autonomy and the capacity for intimacy. As used in TA, *autonomy* refers to the ability to run your own life, to exercise your free will, to be in charge of your own existence. *Intimacy* refers to the ability to love and be loved in return, to have warm and satisfying friendships, and to be able to experience emotional closeness with selected other persons. Clearly, autonomy and intimacy are desirable goals. And Transactional Analysis can contribute to their attainment.

ATTAINING A NORMAL WEIGHT

With the help of this book, you can eventually attain a normal weight, a weight that is right for you in terms of your age, height, and frame. If you are uncertain about what your weight should be, you may wish to consult an authoritative reference book and your physician.

Eric Berne was fond of examples from fairy tales, and he used the related metaphors of the frog and the prince or princess to make his points vivid. It was Berne's view that we are born natural princes and princesses, that most of us—deep down—are OK. However, adversity in the form of insensitive or unloving parents, bad experiences with brothers and sisters, incompetent teachers, and problems with peers may turn the little prince or princess into a frog. And the frog thinks: "I *am* a frog." This is, of course, very sad. He should think: "I am a prince being treated like a frog and I don't care how they treat me, I'm *really* a prince. I'm going to go look for some OK people who will recognize that I'm OK too!"

Similarly, the overeater is likely to identify with a state of "frogginess." He or she thinks: "I *am* a fatso." This, too, is very sad. The overweight person can more productively think: "I *am* a normal person who can attain a normal weight. This excess fat I am carrying is just that—excess baggage. The fact that I have been carrying it for perhaps too long does not mean that it *is* me. I refuse to identify *me* with being fat."

This book asserts that you are *not* destined to be overweight, that you really are a normal-weight prince or princess, that you are basically OK, that most garden-variety obesity is due to overeating, and that a knowledge of TA can help you to break free from fat-making behavior patterns.

2

How Your Parent
Makes You Fat

This chapter is about how your Parent makes you fat. Notice that the word "parent" was capitalized in the previous sentence. In Transactional Analysis, when we speak of the Parent, we are *not* speaking of your actual parents; we are speaking of an ego state within you. An ego state is a kind of subpersonality —a personality within your total personality. Sometimes it takes over and runs your life for a while. Something will push your Parent button, you will go into your Parent ego state, and your behavior will become automatic.

Let's say that a hostess offers you a fattening dessert and says, "I made it just for you." She has pushed your Parent button if you hear yourself saying to yourself, "It wouldn't be polite to say no since she made it just for me." This is probably a replay of something you were taught as a child. When you "hear" in your head things your actual parents or other authority figures said, you are about to enter your Parent ego state. You feel you *must* behave a certain way, whether or not such behavior is in your best interests. There are a number of ways in which your Parent ego state can make you fat, and in this chapter we will explore these ways.

THE PARENT

The Parent is a subpersonality, or ego state, that is *value-oriented*. This is the key to understanding the Parent. The Parent responds in terms of right–wrong, good–bad, yes–no, black–white, success–failure, moral–immoral, pride–guilt, and fattening–nonfattening. As Thomas Harris points out in *I'm OK —You're OK*, the Parent is the *taught* concept of life. If you have studied general psychology, you of course recognize that the Transactional Analysis concept of the Parent is similar to Freud's concept in classical psychoanalysis of the *superego*, the morality-oriented side of our nature. It is correct to say that the Parent and the superego are parallel concepts. However, the difference specified by Eric Berne was that we are *in direct contact with our Parent*. Indeed, we go into our Parent ego state from time to time. Our posture changes, our voice changes, our mental set changes. Hence, the Parent is *not* a hypothesis or a theoretical construction, as is the superego, but a personal reality.

Thus you can know your Parent. You can figure out its characteristics. It is not a big dark secret to you. The information is available, and you can use this information to change your behavior. Further on in this chapter I will offer some practical suggestions for defining the characteristics of your own Parent to yourself.

To complete the personality picture, I am going to jump ahead a bit and give you brief definitions of two more ego states, the Child and the Adult. The Child is the *feeling* side of your personality. When you are in the grips of a strong emotion you have "entered" your Child. Just as certain events, words, and experiences press your Parent button, other stimuli will press your Child button. An example is an insult. When you are insulted, you feel offended, and you are likely to cry or to respond in a hostile manner or just keep it to yourself and feel "one-down." In all these cases, the dominant experience of the moment is a feeling, and you are in your Child. If you associate eating with emotions such as depression, boredom, anger, or anxiety, it is your Child that is making the decision to eat when you feel those feelings. I'll have more to say about the Child and overeating in the next chapter.

The Adult is the ego state that is the *thinking* side of your personality. As such, it is logical, reality-oriented, practical, and able to solve problems. The Adult can plan ahead. The Adult thinks in terms of your long-term welfare, whereas the Child thinks only in terms of the short run. Thus your only hope of losing weight and keeping it off is to find effective ways of entering your Adult *when you want to.* I emphasized "when you want to" because you don't want to be in your Adult all the time. An all-Adult personality would lack spontaneity. He would be like Mr. Spock on *Star Trek*—the unfeeling Vulcan alien who is a living computer. On the contrary, the fully functioning person can and should retain a childlike (not childish!) quality his or her whole life. Very intelligent and creative men and women such as Bertrand Russell, Albert Schweitzer, Albert Einstein, Eleanor Roosevelt, Marie Curie, and Pearl S. Buck all had this childlike quality that is the growing tip of one's existence. No, we wouldn't want to be computer robots unable to enter the Child. However, we want to stay out of the Child ego state when being in the Child can hurt us. When a woman stands in front of the cookie jar and can't stop eating until she has finished all the cookies, she is in her Child. If things like this happen to you, don't be discouraged. There are practical ways of getting out of your Child at such times.

Again, if you're familiar with psychological concepts, you will recognize that the Child is very similar to what psychoanalysts call the *id,* the primal self of the personality. And you will also recognize that the Adult is similar to the ego, the conscious *I* of the personality. Along with the superego, the id and ego in classical psychoanalysis are formal constructs; in Transactional Analysis they are, like the Parent, personal realities. Thus, with Transactional Analysis it is possible to say, "I am in my Child now. And I want to get out. I'm going to enter my Adult." The capacity to do this often creates a clearness of thought that makes it possible for persons to free themselves from self-destructive situations (for example, eating too much at a buffet dinner).

I must remind you that although much of the blame for your personal problems (such as excessive eating) can be attributed to your Parent, the Parent is not the same thing as your actual parent(s). It is made up of values and warnings from your parents and from other authority figures as well, tempered by how you have interpreted the "recordings" of their words and actions. Maybe your parents were great people with great intentions; maybe they weren't. Maybe you heard them wrong. Maybe you were impressed by the wrong things. The point is that it is your Parent that is the culprit here, not your parents. One of the things we want to do is get away from a blaming approach. It is a waste of time to sit around and moan about how if only your parents had treated you differently you wouldn't have the hang-ups you have now. Even if this is in some way true, so what? You're you now, and you can think for yourself from here on out. We want to move on to a problem-solving approach, and you can do this via your Adult.

Don't misunderstand me. The messages recorded in your Parent probably *are* things that your parents or other authority figures said to you. We will soon make an analysis of parental styles and parental messages, but with the idea of liberating you from the past. You don't want to use the past as a rationalization for your present problems. When it becomes clear to you that some of the things in your Parent came from your parents, teachers, older siblings, aunts and uncles, ministers, priests, or rabbis, admired peers, noted authors, and television personalities, don't say, "Oh, that's why I am the way I am. I can't help it. It's all *their* fault. If only they had said or done something else, I would be OK today." Say instead, "Now I see what is behind the way I've been behaving. Now that I see this, I'm free. I can think for myself now and take a new direction."

WHAT YOUR PARENTS SAID

Your actual parents talked to you, with you, and about you. They had a great influence on your development. During childhood you probably identified with them and unconsciously modeled yourself after them in many ways. If, for example, your father was a glutton, you were sent a nonverbal message from his Child to your Child that it's great fun to be a hog. This would be true even if he said from his own Parent, "I don't want to see you become like me. Watch out or you're going to get fat too!" This is called a *duplex message* because he really sends you two messages, one from his Parent in words and another from his Child in his behavior. Both messages are aimed at your Child, but the one you really listen to is the nonverbal behavioral message. Behavior is closer to reality than language; language is more abstract and less convincing to a child than what the child sees with his own eyes.

Roughly speaking, there are three kinds of parent. These are the authoritarian parent, the democratic parent, and the permissive parent. The *authoritarian parent* is the tin-pot dictator. This is the kind of parent who thinks he or she is always right and answers reasonable questions with stock phrases such as: "Because I told you so" or "I'm your father and I've got a right to tell you what to do" or "I'm your mother and you've got to obey me whether you like it or not." The authoritarian parent tends to be hypercritical and is a "put-down" artist. He makes a habit of sending messages from his Parent to the child's Child. Such parents have a great talent for creating problems for their children. "You're getting so fat that I can't stand to look at you anymore. Sometimes I wonder if you're a child of mine" might be a statement coming out of the mouth of an authoritarian mother. This kind of brutal criticism of a child's appearance has, of course, a negative effect. It lowers self-esteem and contributes to eating hang-ups. Such a parent may say in self-defense,

"I'm only trying to help Mary. She could be a beauty queen if only she'd listen to me and use her head to think with instead of for a garbage disposal." But the authoritarian mother is wrong. She is making an *attribution.* An attribution is a statement from the parent that the child has a particular trait. Such attributions have a way of becoming self-fulfilling prophecies. They are intended to be corrective by the parent. However, they often act much like a hex, thus "cursing" the child with unwanted characteristics.

Other examples of attributions made by parents are: "You're lazy," or "You're sloppy," or "You're inconsiderate," or "You're a glutton," or "You're never going to lose weight the way you eat," or "You just don't care how fat you get," or "You inherited my body type—we can't lose weight no matter what we do," or "I think you must have a defective thyroid gland—everything you eat turns to fat." Well, you get the idea. These attributions become part of the child's self-concept. It is a truism in psychology that the person behaves in terms of his self-concept. For example, if a person thinks: "I'm no good at math," he is bound to steer clear of courses in mathematics and be "stupid" when confronted with a mathematical problem. I have taught statistics courses to psychology students who thought of themselves as "no good at math" and have found that their negative self-concept is their worst enemy. Some of these students discovered that their self-concepts were derived from experiences that took place a number of years ago, and making a fresh start, were able to overcome their mathematical liabilities.

So it is with the overweight person who has a poor self-concept stemming from parental attributions. He thinks of himself as hopelessly fat. If you have negative ideas about weight in your self-concept, be aware they are part of your Parent and probably derive from personal statements made to you by your actual parents. Say to yourself, "These attributions are out of date. Maybe that was me *then.* It's not me *now.*" Or say, "My parents overreacted. I wasn't all that bad!"

Let us now consider the permissive parent. The *permissive*

parent makes the mistake of giving the child license where the child should have freedom. The permissive parent completely reverses the traditional parent-child relationship. Instead of being parent-centered, the home becomes child-centered. The child becomes the tin-pot dictator, the tyrant, and mom and dad become slaves to his wishes. Whereas the authoritarian parent tends to produce a compulsive, somewhat neurotic child, the permissive parent tends to produce one who is impulsive and "spoiled." (In more formal psychological language, the permissive parent tends to produce a child with a personality disorder, a rather troublesome person who is egotistical, manipulative, and impulsive, and feels he should always have his own way.) Remember, your Parent ego state represents what you were taught when you were growing up. If you were unfortunate enough to be raised by highly permissive parents, what did they teach you? Through their behavior more than their words, they told you, "The world is your oyster," and "You're better than other people," and "You *can* have your cake and eat it too," and "You really don't have to worry that much about the feelings of other people." Now that you are an adult, your Parent tells you that you are rightfully entitled to all you can grab in life.

How would this affect your eating behavior? It would tend to make you an *impulsive eater* as opposed to a compulsive eater. The impulsive eater is the classic glutton who seems to feel that he has the right to devour the whole world. It is my observation that such a person is usually fatter than the compulsive eater. The reason for this is that he feels little struggle within. It is much harder to do effective psychotherapy or counseling with impulsive eaters than with those who see themselves as struggling with eating problems.

The statistical odds are much higher that you are a compulsive eater rather than an impulsive eater. That's because authoritarian parents are much more common than permissive parents. Then, too, the fact that you are reading this book provides some evidence that you want to do something about your eating behavior. Most of what I have to say to you in this book is based on the assumption that you have a strong conscious wish to lose weight. Thus the book is addressed more to the compulsive eater than to the impulsive eater. If you are distressed by being fat, are unhappy with your eating behavior, and *do not* believe that fat is beautiful, then read on.

Finally, there is the democratic parent. You are fortunate indeed if you had democratic parents. The *democratic parent* gives his or her child freedom, but not license. The home has structure, but it is not a prison. There is room to grow, to stretch, to find oneself. I highly recommend the books *Between Parent & Child* by Haim Ginott and *Parent Effectiveness Training* by Thomas Gordon for clear examples of the democratic style of parenting.

If your parents were generally democratic, it is doubtful that you will have much of a problem with food. Your attitude toward food tends to be neither compulsive nor impulsive, but *spontaneous.* You can "take it or leave it." If you have a weight problem, you probably have no more than a ten- or twenty-pound problem. The weight has sneaked up on you because of lack of vigilance. But you are not really a compulsive eater. You can "make up your mind" and "use your will power" when you are sufficiently motivated. This is another way of saying you have a good strong Adult that can take charge when it decides to.

THE COMPOSITION OF THE PARENT

Very few of us, of course, had "pure" parents. Most parents operate in a mixture of authoritarian, permissive, and democratic styles. Thus most persons have Parent ego states composed of three facets: (1) the Controlling Parent, (2) the Permissive Parent, and (3) the Nurturing Parent.

Your parents probably had a dominant mode of acting and reacting, and this will be reflected in what is the largest single facet of your Parent. For example, we might say that Eleanor has a large Controlling Parent, a small Permissive Parent, and a small Nurturing Parent. On the other hand, we might say that Tom has a small Controlling Parent, a large Permissive Parent, and a small Nurturing Parent.

If you have a large Controlling Parent, the dominant parental style under which you were raised was probably authoritarian. If you have a large Permissive Parent, your parents' dominant style was likely to have been permissive. If you have a large Nurturing Parent, the dominant style of your parents was probably democratic.

This classification scheme derives primarily from traditional TA theory. In his writings, Berne clearly identifies the Controlling Parent and the Nurturing Parent. However, the concept of the Permissive Parent is not to my knowledge a part of established TA theory. The concept is nonetheless perfectly plausible in terms of what we know about child development. Some parents are too permissive, giving their children license to act out feelings and obey impulses without sufficient limits. Such treatment will logically foster the formation of a large Permissive Parent.

To summarize in terms of these ego states, if you have a large Controlling Parent that harps at you about the way you eat and what you eat and makes you feel constantly guilty about food and fat, you will tend to be the classic compulsive eater. If you have a large Permissive Parent that gives you too much permission to indulge yourself, you will tend to be an unrestrained impulsive eater. If you have a large Nurturing Parent, you will have a minimal amount of eating problems and a maximal chance of correcting those you do have.

WHAT DOES YOUR PARENT SAY NOW?

I have asked my clients this question: What does your Parent say now about eating? You might pause and reflect for a moment. How would you answer the question? Here are some typical responses from clients:

1. Eat three square meals a day.
2. Clean your plate.
3. Don't waste food.
4. Don't eat between meals.
5. Eat balanced meals.
6. Don't skip meals.
7. Eat a hearty breakfast.

The above injunctions seem to be self-evident truths. They are a part of almost all Parent ego states. They seem to be good advice about healthful eating. It may surprise you to discover that *each one of the injunctions can be fat-making!*

Let's analyze each one to see why this is so.

Eat three square meals a day. Almost all of us feel that we're entitled to a breakfast, a lunch, and a dinner every day. The overweight person particularly tends to be programmed. His Parent says it's OK to have breakfast, lunch, or dinner *if it is time to eat.* The problem eater does not ask himself, "Am I hungry?" Instead he asks, "What time is it?" If the clock says it is eating time, then he eats. And what is a "square" meal? It is a *complete* meal. Do you really need three complete meals every day? Have you ever noticed how slim people occasionally skip a meal? Ask them why. They will answer, "I'm just not hungry right now." Many obese persons never skip a meal. They may not have hunger, *but they always have appetite.*

Actually, the concept of three square meals had its origin in the days when people lived on farms and needed energy for a hard day's work. As the population of the United States has moved from the rural areas to the urban zones, there has been a decrease in the total amount of food needed by the average person. If your Parent says, "Eat three square meals a day," and you lead a somewhat sedentary life, your Parental programming is out of date. You need three square meals about as much as Eskimos need ice cubes.

Clean your plate. Did your parents make you feel bad if you left food on your plate? Or worse, did they actually insist that you always "lick your platter clean"? Do you today feel guilty if you leave food on your plate? If you answered these questions "Yes," you are not alone. When I was in the military, there were signs in our chow hall that said: "Take all you want, but eat all you take." Sometimes a master sergeant would post himself by a garbage can. Men who approached the can with a tray containing a half-eaten slice of bread or a pie crust or a partially consumed scoop of mashed potatoes were ordered back to their tables. In this instance, the military and the master sergeant were acting as superparents. Childhood training, military pressures, boarding school rules, and experiences from many similar settings have provided countless millions of people with the subconscious message "Always clean your plate."

Well, *should* you always clean your plate? Of course not! There are many, many times when an adult may decide that he has either taken too much food or been given too much food. If you have eaten two-thirds of the food on your plate, feel full, want no more, and are overweight, it is really quite absurd to stuff yourself because your Parent says, "Eat it all!" Ask.yourself, "What does my Adult say?" If your Adult says, "I've had enough. I would be forcing myself if I ate everything on the plate," then listen to your Adult (your reality-oriented self) and feel free to leave some food on the plate. If you are at home, you can of course save the uneaten food as part of the leftovers. But what if you are a guest in someone's home or you are in a restaurant? Won't the food go to waste? And isn't it a sin to waste food? This brings us to our next maxim.

Don't waste food. This statement seems so clear, correct, and obvious that there would appear to be nothing to discuss. Like many messages recorded in the Parent, it is accepted without question. Indeed, I agree with it. In these times when there is a worldwide food shortage, it *is* wrong to waste food. But what does it mean to "waste" food? Is food wasted only if it is thrown away? Is it not also wasted if it is swallowed into a fat body? If you eat beyond your needs, aren't you wasting the food too? Indeed, isn't it even more wasteful than throwing it into the garbage pail? If you are destroying your body, shortening your life, and incapacitating one of the parents of your children (yourself), aren't you wasting food? Thus it merely becomes a question of which garbage pail you are going to throw the food into—a human garbage pail or a literal garbage pail. When looked at this way, many people begin to recognize it is not so wrong to "waste" food and let some of it go into the garbage can or the garbage disposal.

I encourage people when they go out to restaurants to leave some food on the plate. For example, eat half of the baked potato, half of a slice of bread, half of a dessert. In my weight-control classes the first reaction to this suggestion is often: "Oh, I couldn't do that!" On investigation, it usually turns out that the person who protests has Parent messages that say "Don't waste food" or "Think of the starving people in India" (or Indochina or Africa.) *Stop and think!* Will it help the suffering people of the world if you take the second half of the baked potato, finish the slice of bread, or consume the balance of the dessert? You sure are doing them a big favor by getting fat! They will really thank you for your altruism! No, really, it is no more wasteful to let food be thrown out than thrown into a fat body. I repeat: It is only a question of which garbage pail it is going into.

Don't eat between meals. The Parent of the problem eater often contains the injunction "Don't eat between meals." Now, the overweight person often *does* eat between meals (the Parent is not necessarily obeyed), but he feels guilty while doing so. Because he feels guilty, he often eats between meals like a sneak thief. He may stand in front of the refrigerator, the door open, eating simultaneously from several dishes or bowls. Or he may stand in front of the pantry gobbling crackers, peanut butter, and potato chips. The furtive characteristics of the behavior are made worse by the internal voice from the Parent that is saying, "What's wrong with you? Don't you know you shouldn't be eating between meals? You had a good lunch and we're going to have dinner in an hour. You shouldn't be hungry." Seldom do we challenge the doctrine that we shouldn't eat between meals. We feel that the voice of the Parent is right and we are wrong.

But is the Parent right? The idea that we should eat only three meals and not eat between those meals is just one more unexamined Parent message. Research with animals indicates that it might be preferable to eat six small meals per day instead of three large ones. Some lines of investigation suggest that man, like his early primate ancestors, is a born nibbler. If food were to be consumed six or seven times a day in small amounts, it would be better for blood sugar levels and easier on our pancreas than the present mode of larger amounts consumed in three sittings.

If you like to eat between meals, this kind of eating may have greater psychological bearing on your weight problem than the way you eat at meals. Many overweight persons find it relatively easy to control their meal eating, but not their snack eating. If you happen to be in this category, I suggest that you challenge your Parent. Here and now decide: "It's OK to eat between meals." But won't this make you fatter? Well, will it? That's what your Parent says.

There are in fact many nonfattening ways to eat between meals. One of the easiest is to eat somewhat less at meals and leave room for a snack. One of my clients used always to have a small salad with his lunch. Now he eats his lunch without the salad and takes time out for it at three or four o'clock. Another client, a homemaker, used to eat sandwiches with white bread for lunch. She has discovered that she has no real craving for white bread, but she does crave cookies. She would try to resist the cookies, but would break down in the afternoon and eat eight or ten in a few minutes while standing in the kitchen. All the while she was eating the cookies, her Parent kept pounding away at her: "What's wrong with you? Do you want to stay fat like this? You're really a mess!"

I gave her "permission" to eat cookies and to eat them between meals. I told her to eliminate the white bread with lunch. It was determined that the ideal psychological time for her to eat the cookies was at four o'clock in the afternoon. She was to place two cookies on a plate, take the plate to the kitchen table, turn off the television set, do no reading while eating, and give the cookies her full and complete attention. She was to concentrate on eating, making the event a sensuous experience. Using this approach, she was satisfied with the two cookies. Look at the advantages. Before, she was eating two slices of white bread with lunch and eight to ten cookies. Now she was eating a light lunch and two cookies. Psychologically she was more satisfied, and she had cut down her total caloric intake.

In my own case, I happen to have no craving for a midmorning snack. However, I often crave an afternoon snack and a late evening snack. For years I felt guilty about this and tried to fight it with iron will power. The result? Total failure. One day it occurred to me to "use judo" on my compulsions, that is, to *go with* the energy in an overwhelming urge, not fight against that energy. So now I allow myself to eat five times a day without guilt! However, I *do* cut down on what I eat at meals. I seldom eat bread with lunch or dinner. I do not have desserts with meals. My snacks are usually low in sugar and starch and high in protein. However, my Child does sometimes crave sweets, and I will talk about coping with the Child's cravings in the next chapter.

Eat balanced meals. Yes, we *do* need a balanced diet. We need to get a proper amount of protein, fat, carbohydrates, vitamins, and minerals. But we do not need everything with *every meal.* A particular meal may be unbalanced without long-term ill effects. For example, one client craved pie à la mode about once a week. Her Parent said, "That's awful. You're fifteen pounds overweight. You can't have any pie or ice cream until you lose the excess weight." This, of course, only compounded her problem. She craved the treat intensely, broke down, ate it, felt guilty, and still craved more pie and ice cream. Eating guiltily, she did *not* get full psychological satisfaction from the food. I suggested she have pie à la mode for her dinner once a week.

"Oh, no!" she protested. "I can't do that!"

"Why not?"

"It's wrong!"

"Why is it wrong?"

"Because we need a balanced diet!"

"Do you really think if you have pie à la mode for dinner once a week you will unbalance your diet?"

"Well, pie and ice cream are fattening."

"Don't you think it is more fattening to eat a regular dinner followed by pie and ice cream than it is to eat pie and ice cream alone?"

She reflected. Finally she said, "I see what you mean."

"Can you see how you've been reacting in terms of Parent messages that are at best half-truths, not whole truths?"

"Yes. I really haven't been thinking for myself."

"That's right. When we play old Parent tapes and obey them slavishly, we are like programmed robots, not aware human beings."

To repeat, we *do,* of course, need to eat well-balanced meals. But your Parent is *not* correct if it says every single meal you eat must be well-balanced.

Don't skip meals. Many persons have a Parent that says it is wrong to skip meals. As a general rule, it probably is unwise to skip meals. In order to stabilize blood sugar and avoid hypoglycemia (chronic low blood sugar), it is better to take in a little food often than take in a lot of food once or twice a day. However, there *are* times when it is OK to skip a meal. Let us say something has made you angry and you "have knots in your stomach." It is lunchtime. Should you force yourself to eat because your Parent says, "Don't skip meals"? Of course not. Ask your Adult to make a realistic appraisal of the situation. If your Adult says it would be wiser to skip lunch or wait until later, listen to your practical Adult, not your moralizing Parent.

In Loma Linda, California, there is a large and world-famous university medical center. The School of Nutrition and Public

Health at Loma Linda has experimented with various eating plans for obese persons and have found that for some individuals (not all, of course), a practical plan is to skip dinner entirely. It seems that many overweight people find it easier to fast or semifast than to restrict the quantity they are accustomed to eating at a meal. One man I know slims down by cutting out lunches. I think he would be better off if he had a glass of nonfat milk in place of the lunch; the nonfat milk has food value and helps maintain an optimal blood sugar level. In any event, my point is simply that there may be certain conditions under which it would be appropriate for you to skip a meal. It may not generally be a good idea, maybe you shouldn't do it often—but the notion that it is wrong to skip a meal is not necessarily a Universal Truth. You need guidelines, not rigid rules. Unfortunately, if you have a Controlling Parent, it tends to issue dogmatic orders, not guidelines with a bit of latitude. Again, learn to listen to your Adult and start thinking for yourself.

Eat a hearty breakfast. Well, of course, everyone knows that breakfast is the most important meal of the day. Don't all parents, physicians, nutritionists, nurses, dieticians, and health experts say so? No; some authorities declare that this is just one more myth perpetuated by constant repetition. You see, *nothing is all-true for everybody.* It might be true that breakfast is the most important meal of the day for 80 percent or 90 percent or even 95 percent of the population. It might *not* be true for you. You are an individual, you have your own body rhythm and metabolic rate. I have worked with clients who loathe breakfast. One of these clients forced herself for years to eat a breakfast with cereal, juice, fruit, toast, bacon, and eggs every day. She thought it was the "right" thing to do. Her Controlling Parent said, "Susan, you've got to have energy for the day. Breakfast is your most important meal." Yet she would have been satisfied with a piece of toast, one or two strips of bacon, and a cup of coffee. In view of the fact that she was thirty pounds overweight, it was absurd for her to be loading herself down with extra food every morning.

In this section I have tried to show that many of the things we have been taught about eating are only partial truths at best. Even what seems to be the very best advice from our parents and other authority figures can be fat-making if listened to in a nonthinking fashion. Good advice becomes a part of your Parent, and you must—if you are to be a thinking person—ask yourself if it is really good advice or just good-sounding advice. There is a difference. And we must learn to discriminate.

DIET IS A FOUR-LETTER WORD

The phrase "four-letter word" is often used to describe so-called nasty words, and I must admit that in my lexicon "diet" has become a negative and somewhat nasty word. The whole concept of "going on a diet" is a Parent concept. Your Parent says to you, "You're getting too fat. You're getting to be a slob! You've got to get hold of yourself. I'm putting you on a diet." So you put yourself in psychological prison. From the first day you feel you are suffering. The whole thing is an agony of deprivation. You are living for the day when you can go off the diet. (Note that "going on a diet" implies "going off a diet." The Parent uses black–white thinking that tells you a person is either on a diet or off a diet.)

Now, while you are on a diet you are repressing your Child. Anything the Child wants (such as a treat or a snack) is "wrong" or "bad." The temptation to cheat grows. If you cheat (and most people on a diet do), you see yourself as "bad." This is the stern judgment of your Parent as it looks down on your Child.

After two days or two weeks or two months your Child rebels! The harder your Parent has been on your Child, the more likely you are to "go wild" and binge without control. This is why diets seldom work in the long run. Sad to say, the vast majority of overweight people gain back all the weight they lose on a diet and more! The whole thing is a self-defeating witch's circle that gets you nowhere, and it is a circle that must be broken if you are to lose weight and keep it off for good.

Don't say from your Parent, "I'm going to go on a diet." Say from your thinking Adult, "I'm going to improve some of my eating habits. I'm going to trim off some calories and carbohydrates here and there—wherever and whenever I can." Ignore your Critical Parent if it makes pronouncements such as: "You're never going to eat anything with refined sugar in it again." Unfortunately, some weight-control self-help groups preach this philosophy. I know from working with many ex-members of one of these groups that such a rigid philosophy leads to psychological suffering and guilty binges. From your Adult say to yourself, "I'm going to cut down, but not cut out. All foods are acceptable in moderation."

"But I can't eat certain foods in moderation," you may protest. "If I even eat a small amount of candy or pizza, I go on an uncontrollable spree." I know what you mean. I was the same way once. So were many of my clients. Why is this such a common problem with overweight people? Do they suffer from chronic suicidal tendencies? Are they victims of Freud's death instinct? Are they unconsciously trying to kill themselves with food? I don't think so. I think they are caught in a double bind between the Critical Parent and the Impulsive Child. They have to learn how to end the war between the Parent and the Child. There are ways. And as we progress in the book, these ways will become clearer and clearer to you.

CONTACTING YOUR PARENT

The first step in freeing yourself from your Parent's domination is to make conscious contact with your Parent ego state. One way of doing this is to ask yourself a set of reflective questions. Try to answer the questions in as much depth as possible. Go back over them after several days or weeks and try to answer them again. I particularly suggest that you put your answers *in writing*. You can think things through on paper in a way that is not possible on a purely mental level. Take your thoughts out of your mind and make them concrete on paper. Here are some questions that may help you contact your Parent:

1. Do you tend to "go into" your Parent often?
2. What were some of the things you learned from authority figures other than your actual parents?
3. Did your parents often address themselves to your Child ego state?
4. What was the dominant style of your parents—authoritarian, democratic, or permissive?
5. Did your parents in various ways "hex" you and make the prediction that you would be fat? Has this become a message in your Parent?
6. What are some of the attributions about you that have become part of your Parent? List two or three "bad" traits that have become part of your self-image. Conversely, list two or three "good" traits that have become part of your self-image.
7. What does your Parent say about your body type?
8. Does your Parent say that you are entitled to as much food as you can eat?
9. Does your Parent make you feel guilty about what you eat, when you eat, why you eat, how you eat, and where you eat? Is your inner Parent a "put-down artist" that more often than not makes you feel bad about eating?

COPING WITH YOUR PARENT

Once you have made clear contact with your Parent, know where it is coming from, and know what it wants for you, it is possible to cope with your Parent. Only your inner Adult can cope with the Parent. There are three basic ways your realistic Adult can cope with a Controlling Parent. These are: (1) turning off the Parent, (2) challenging the Parent, and (3) not listening to the Parent. Let's examine each of these psychological strategies individually.

Turning off the Parent. Sometimes when a Parental tape begins to play you can actually visualize a tape recorder and hear in your mind the voice of an authority figure. "Oh, yes, tape No. 21," you think. "It seems to me I've heard that song before." In your mind's eye imagine a hand reaching out to the tape recorder. The hand moves the recorder switch from the "on" position to the "off" position. The offending Parental message has been decisively turned off. Try it. You will be surprised at how effective this bit of mental imagery can be.

Challenging the Parent. If you think a Parental maxim is working against your best interests, examine it by asking yourself: Is it based on false assumptions? Is it a hasty generalization? Is it outmoded and inappropriate advice for me today? If the answer to any of these questions is yes, then by all means challenge your Parent. Imagine your Adult saying to your Parent, "I've believed that maxim for years without really thinking about it. Now I think it's illogical [or outmoded, or whatever]." If your Parent answers back (and it probably will), continue the inner dialogue. It may even be necessary for your Adult to talk sternly to a particularly domineering Parent. You might say, "You represent what I have been taught. Not everything I was taught as a child and adolescent is right for me. From now on I am putting my Adult in charge and thinking for myself."

Not listening to the Parent. We have all seen children use this technique with their parents. The child's eyes go blank or drift off to a corner of the room. Eye contact is lost, and so is the child's attention. The parent feels he is speaking to the wall; his words "fall on deaf ears" or "go in one ear and out the other." You can obviously use the same technique with your inner Parent. When it begins to send you worn-out maxims, put-downs of your character, and other useless messages, think to yourself: "I hear some words, but I'm not listening. It's all going in one ear and out the other. I'm not a child now, and I don't have to listen as a child is supposed to listen." Mentally picture the words going in one ear and out the other ear in unchanged form.

I must admit I've been pretty hard on the Parent in this section. Actually, your Parent is not all bad. Of course not. Your Parent contains a great deal of sense. And you should listen to the sense. Unfortunately, most Parents also contain a good deal of nonsense—much of it fat-making—and the job of your Adult is to separate the sense from the nonsense. Note that as I have been talking about coping with the Parent, I have been talking about controlling messages. These are the messages you want to either turn off or challenge or not listen to. In order to lose weight and keep it off, it is very helpful to free yourself from the influence of either a Controlling Parent or a Permissive Parent.

3

How Your Child
Makes You Fat

Perhaps you are convinced from reading Chapter Two that the Parent is the main villain of the piece where fat-making behavior is concerned. Not so! Your inner Child plays as large a part in making you fat as your Parent does. The father of Gestalt therapy, Frederick ("Fritz") Perls, specified two parts to the human personality: the top dog and the underdog. He called these the two clowns of the personality. They are always playing games and trying to get the better of each other. The top dog and the underdog are, of course, just other names for what Transactional Analysis refers to as the Controlling Parent and the Child. The Controlling Parent is analogous to the top dog and the Child is analogous to the underdog. The Controlling Parent tries to dominate, influence, control, and dominate the Child. The Child won't take this kind of treatment in the long run. (It may agree to take it for the short run.) When the Child has "had it," there is rebellion, and this rebellion plays a large part in problem eating. In this chapter I will specify a number of ways your Child makes you fat.

THE CHILD

The Child is a subpersonality, or ego state, that is *feeling-oriented*. Like the Parent, it is archaic in that it is based on "recordings" of the past. The difference between the Parent and the Child is that the recordings in the Parent are *cognitive* —that is, they consist of conscious verbal messages—and the recordings in the Child are nonverbal. The Child "tapes" present gut-level data. Thus the Child is more primitive than the Parent, harder to know at a conscious level, and somewhat more difficult to cope with. Nonetheless, the Child *can* be known, and its power over the whole person can be reduced.

The Child tends to be very much like an actual child of preschool age, a child that has not yet reached the age of reason. Such a child is magical in his or her thinking, impulsive, highly emotional, and oriented toward fantasy. This same child that you once were is carried forward in your personality as your Child ego state. When you are in a very bad mood, or a very good mood, your Adult lowers its guard and you tend to go into your Child.

It is probably not much of a surprise to hear that you go into your Child when you are in a bad mood. Many overweight people recognize that they crave food when they are "low"— when they are anxious, bored, tense, nervous, worried, or depressed. What is somewhat less obvious is the tendency to overeat when one is "high." A good party, a picnic, a vacation, visiting friends, enjoying a movie, special occasions, and holidays—any of these situations seems to set the stage for careless eating. I call such eating *impulsive eating* to contrast it with the more well-known term *compulsive eating*. The happy Child is an impulsive eater. There is no thought for tomorrow. The long-run consequences of eating too much are set aside. The only thing that is important is the pleasure of the present moment. It is well to be aware of the phenomenon of impulsive eating, to name it, and to watch out for it. Such awareness brings the Adult into the act and sets up a counterforce to the irresponsible Child.

THE COMPOSITION OF THE CHILD

Like the Parent, the Child is composed of three facets. In *What Do You Say After You Say Hello?*, Berne identifies these as: (1) the Adapted Child, (2) the Rebellious Child, and (3) the Natural Child. In addition, we all share to a greater or lesser degree a part of the Child called the *Little Professor.*

As an actual child, you had a dominant mode of acting and reacting, and this dominant mode is reflected in the largest single facet of your Child ego state. For example, we might say that Pamela has a large Adapted Child, a small Rebellious Child, and a small Natural Child. On the other hand, we might say that William has a small Adapted Child, a large Rebellious Child, and a small Natural Child.

Persons with a large *Adapted Child* far outnumber those with a large Rebellious Child or a large Natural Child. The person with a large Adapted Child felt forced to "purchase" affection when he or she was an actual child. The odds are that such a person felt his parents wouldn't love him unless he adapted to their demands—thus the term Adapted Child. If you developed a large Adapted Child in your early life, you are probably today the kind of person who tends to give in to the wishes of people who are more assertive or aggressive than you are. Too often you find yourself saying "Yes" when you want to say "No."

This pattern is exhibited by many overweight people. They tend to be "nice" people—polite, law-abiding, overly responsible, nonoffensive in human relations, excessively modest, apologetic, and likable. All these characteristics point to the existence of a large Adapted Child. One of the few areas in which they can be wayward and defiant is in the area of eating. Unnecessary eating is often regarded unconsciously as a form of autonomy, a declaration of personal freedom. "You can't tell me what to do!" says the fat husband or wife as he or she sneaks a second piece of cake. Of course, this kind of assertiveness is only pseudo-assertiveness; it is the pathetic rebellion of one who feels at a deeper level the inability to stand up for one's rights.

People with a large Adapted Child are too concerned with the good opinion of others. They are chronically uptight about being liked, being accepted. Unfortunately, they tend to equate being a liked person with being a respected person. Thus the person with a large Adapted Child often builds up a huge stroke hunger. You will recall from Chapter One that the term *stroke* is used in TA to refer to any kind of affection, attention, or recognition from another human being. Strokes tell you that you exist. Without them you would feel like an invisible being. The concept of strokes derives from the time when you were an infant, from the days when your parents held you, cuddled you, and gave you real physical strokes. Such strokes are essential to normal human development. René Spitz, a researcher who studied the development of infants in institutions, discovered that socially isolated babies are weepy and frail, and exhibit a high death rate. And this has nothing to do with nutrition. The babies are well fed. What they are suffering from is a lack of human interest in their welfare.

Harry Harlow, a former president of the American Psychological Association and a leading investigator into the behavior of primates, has found that monkeys reared in social isolation develop severely disturbed personalities. They run from the slightest noise and spend countless hours rocking in corners like autistic children. When raised on mother surrogates made of wood, sponge rubber, and terry cloth, they run and cling to their "mothers" as if they had life. If we can generalize to human beings, Harlow's research suggests the incredible need we have for affection. Harlow suggests the term *affectional drive* to indicate the existence in organisms of a need for the psychological attention of another organism.

We never outgrow our need for strokes. Our Child craves strokes every day. The physical strokes we need as infants give way to a need for psychological strokes as we mature. We associate being attended to with actual stroking because as infants our parents were paying attention to us when they were stroking us. The preschooler's frequent call of "Look at me!" is the precursor of striving for degrees, honors, status, medals, certificates, position, or prestige as an adult. All these items represent our great need for strokes.

I said that the person with a large Adapted Child tends to build up a huge stroke hunger. Why? The person with a large Adapted Child never seems to get enough strokes because he is never quite convinced that (1) he is entitled to the stroke he gets, and (2) there are more strokes coming. Remember, he had to *earn* strokes as a child. Being loved was *conditional.* Therefore at the deepest level of his being lurks the doubt: *Am I really worthy of being stroked?* The answer often seems to be no. To such persons, strokes are like money. They must be worked for, saved, and "spent" with due consideration.

Persons with a large Adapted Child often turn to food when they are in a state of stroke hunger, when they feel they are insufficiently appreciated, recognized, or loved. But why? Why is the act of eating equated with being stroked? It is all a matter of conditioning. As an infant you were held when you were fed. When you were held you were being stroked and attended to. As an older infant you were spoon-fed in the high chair. Eating time was a time when your parents looked at you, played with you, and talked to you. Perhaps as an older child your parents paid a great deal of attention to your eating behavior. They noted how much you ate, how fast you ate, whether or not you had good table manners, and so forth. Your Child is thus conditioned to accept the following formula: food = being attended to = strokes. It is thus a very small wonder that a person with a large Adapted Child turns to food when the psychological road gets rough. Unnecessary eating is a form of self-stroking designed to reduce a state of stroke hunger.

The person with a large *Rebellious Child* is much less complex in his eating behavior than the person with a large Adapted Child. The Rebellious Child within leads him to eat without restraint and without guilt. Whereas individuals with a large Adapted Child are oversocialized, those with a large Rebellious Child are undersocialized. They tend in other areas of their behavior to be boorish, overtalkative, rude, inconsiderate, and selfish. Superobese persons, persons who weigh 300 pounds and more, are very often the owners of a large Rebellious Child. When I first started working with overweight persons, I thought that the fatter people were, the more neurotic they tended to be. I have corrected my first impression. The superobese seem to suffer from a minimum of inner conflict over eating too much. Of course, they *do* wail publicly about their problem, but much of this is a pose—a social mask—designed to elicit sympathy. They seek excuses for their behavior. But more often than not, there is a minimum of good faith in their effort to reduce. This is why superobese people are so hard to work with in psychotherapy. They don't seem to have enough internal distress to energize the therapy; that is, they have little real motivation to work on their problem. These are the people who resort to long fasts in hospitals and bypass operations. The Rebellious Child does not want to listen to a rational approach to weight control. However, this individual may crave from time to time a slim body. When this wish becomes dominant, the Rebellious Child says, "I want it now! And I want it without working for it." We may note that this kind of demand on the part of the Rebellious Child has something to do with the enormous success of obesity specialists who push various kinds of drugs for weight control. The Rebellious Child suffers from the fantasy that the drug will allow unrestricted eating along with magical weight loss.

The person with a large *Natural Child* is the best off when it comes to food and eating. The Natural Child does not make a powerful connection between food and strokes. It sees food as food and strokes as strokes, and does not look for something in food that isn't there. Thus the person with a large Natural Child is in the fortunate position of having a "take it or leave it" attitude toward food. He eats to live; he does not live to eat.

We may summarize our comparison of the Adapted Child, the Rebellious Child, and the Natural Child by use of the following illustration:

IMPULSIVE EATING SPONTANEOUS EATING COMPULSIVE EATING

I ——————————— I ——————————— I

Rebellious Child   Natural Child   Adapted Child

As you can see, the spectrum of possible eating behavior under the influence of the Child ranges from impulsive eating at one end of the pole to compulsive eating at the other. The spontaneous eating behavior of the Natural Child represents an optimal position between two extremes. It stands for the freedom to eat what we want to eat *and* the freedom to *not* eat what we don't want to eat. It is the goal toward which I will try to direct you as we develop additional concepts in future chapters.

THE LITTLE PROFESSOR

The Little Professor is the intuitive dimension of the Child. This is not meant in a mystical sense. It is simply the down-to-earth ability of the Child to perceive body talk, gestures, facial expressions, tone of voice, and other nonverbal cues as a kind of communication. For example, a mother says to her child, "I love you." The Adapted Child, wanting love, agrees, "She loves me." But the Little Professor in the Child is more analytical, critical, and objective about the message (thus the term Little Professor). The Little Professor notes that the tone of voice is wrong. The mother is speaking mechanically, saying what she thinks her child wants to hear. There is love in her words, but no love in her voice.

Transfer this kind of psychological relationship to adulthood. Let us say that a husband is leaving for work. "Do you love me?" asks his wife, hoping for a stroke. "Of course I love you," he replies absently as he pecks her on the cheek and rushes off. If the wife is really suffering from a substantial stroke hunger, she will try to accept the bone he threw to her. But the Little Professor objects! "His response was wooden. There was no enthusiasm in his voice. There was no warmth in his look." The Little Professor will not allow uncritical acceptance of mere words. An hour or two after breakfast the wife in question may find herself snacking for "no reason." She is stroking her hurt Child, trying to make the Child feel good.

The Little Professor keeps the Child from being entirely gullible. Thus we want to tune in to the Little Professor. In relating to others, we want to be aware of the importance of body talk and other kinds of nonverbal cues. However, we also want to get the Adult into the picture. The Little Professor's analysis will push the Child button, and we will start to feel bad on the basis of an *incomplete* analysis. Remember, the Little Professor is a part of the Child, and its analysis is a Child's analysis. The wife who was told, "Of course I love you," in a perfunctory manner, should have plugged into her Adult by asking herself a few objective questions: "Was Tom in a hurry this morning? Is he worried about something? Is he generally distant and unaffectionate—or is this morning's behavior out of character?" The Little Professor makes us sensitive, and it is well that we are sensitive. However, by using the Adult, we can keep ourselves from being oversensitive.

TRADING STAMPS AND RACKETS

The theory of Transactional Analysis proposes that we collect psychological trading stamps the same way we collect actual trading stamps issued by merchants. Two kinds of psychological trading stamps are collected: brown stamps and gold stamps. Brown stamps are collected when we allow ourselves to be used or put down by others. They give us feelings of depression, emptiness, meaninglessness, frustration, and demoralization. Gold stamps are collected when we volunteer ourselves in the service of others, such as going out of our way to do a favor or giving an outstanding party. They give us feelings of pride, status, exultation—feelings that say, "I'm better than they are." Gold stamps are the favorite stamps of vain people.

Both kinds of stamps may be used to make you fat, depending upon your particular racket or rackets. A racket in TA is a recurring, self-indulgent behavior pattern in which you get to trade in some of your stamps. Let's say that you have collected a lot of brown stamps. You are depressed and demoralized— and none of it is your fault! The brown stamps entitle you to a guilt-free eating binge. You have a right to eat, you rationalize, because you feel bad. (And it's not your fault you feel bad.) Perhaps you allow yourself desserts and sweets when things are not going well. Or maybe you feel entitled to second and third helpings as a balm to the soul. There are many ways of trading in brown stamps, and many variations on the basic racket of using brown stamps to "buy" food.

Let's say that you have recently collected a lot of gold stamps. Now you can use the gold stamps to reward yourself. We are all familiar with the fact that food is used to celebrate events. In the same way, gold stamps allow us to have minicelebrations. A fat homemaker may have worked hard to throw a successful party. After all the guests leave, she is glowing. They were lavish in their praise of her home, her food, her taste in decorations, etc. She has collected several pages (maybe a whole book) of gold stamps. Before she goes to bed she cuts herself a huge piece of cake and announces to her husband, "I'm going to have a second piece of cake tonight. I think I deserve it!" Her collection of gold stamps allows her to eat beyond her bodily needs without guilt. Trading in gold stamps for unnecessary food is as much of a racket as trading in brown stamps for unnecessary food.

It is the Child, of course, that collects stamps—brown or gold —and indulges in rackets. As long as these processes remain unnamed and unspecified, we are at their mercy. On the other hand, if we stand back a bit, reflect, and use the Adult, we have some chance of busting our own rackets.

You can bust rackets by learning to say to yourself from your Adult, "I'm bingeing now because my Child is trading in some brown stamps. Do I want to allow my Child to be in this kind of fat-making racket? Do I really want to trade in my brown stamps for fat?" Or say to yourself, "I'm eating this dessert because I've collected a lot of gold stamps, and my Child is rewarding itself with food. This is a racket too! Just like trading in brown stamps! These rackets bring me short-term pleasure in the form of eating, but long-run pain—in the form of fat." This kind of conscious realistic thinking from the Adult can do a lot toward nixing fat-making rackets.

FRIENDS AND YOUR CHILD

Let us say that Mary is out shopping with her friend Susan. They stop at a snack bar, and Susan orders a piece of pie. Mary is trying to lose weight and orders only coffee. Susan cuts her piece of pie in half and offers it to Mary with the words, "You've got to help me out with this. It's too much for me and we can't let it go to waste." Mary feels cornered and helpless. She takes the pie with a meek "Thank you," and forces herself to eat it. What has happened? Mary has allowed herself to be intimidated by Susan. Susan comes on as the Controlling Parent, and she is addressing herself to Mary's Child. If Mary has a large Adapted Child—as so many of us do—she is overly concerned with Susan's approval. Again, there is the unconscious feeling that the friendship is not truly merited, that one is not liked for one's own sake, and that affection is conditional. Thus Mary "buys" Susan's friendship by small acts of subservience or by doing Susan various favors.

Over and over and over again, you will find your friends addressing themselves directly to your Child. You must be alert to the fact that it is very common in friendships for one person to assume the role of Parent and the other person to assume the role of Child. This peculiarity of human relationships becomes particularly important if it is an element in your life that is contributing to your weight problem. (And it often is!) To provide another illustration of how a Parent-Child friendship can be fat-making, let's say that Mary and her husband are dinner guests at the home of another couple. Throughout the entire visit Mary finds herself assaulted with a series of statements such as: "I made it just for you," or "I'll feel hurt if you don't take more than that," or "You've got to sample the rice," or "You just can't pass up my strawberry cheesecake." The amount of psychological pressure that can be brought to bear on us when we are visiting friends is slightly short of incredible. Persons who crave approval will often eat things they don't want so as not to offend the host or hostess.

What is happening here? You must recognize that *you are on someone else's territory* when you are a guest. This automatically places you in the one-down position and the host and hostess in the one-up position. Thus it is very easy for them to play Parent to your Child. If you are suffering from a stroke-hunger, this will make your Adapted Child excessively anxious to please others, and you will find yourself purchasing strokes by eating too much and being a good little guest.

You also have to realize that in many cases *your friends prefer that you remain fat.* In theory, friends have your best interests at heart. This is true if your relationship with a friend is Adult-Adult. Unfortunately, most friendships are pseudo-friendships, and instead of being Adult-Adult are Parent-Child. In a Parent-Child "friendship" there is a tacit agreement that one person gets to pull the strings and the other person gets to jump. What does the string-puller get out of such a relationship? The string-puller gets a *sense of power*. What does the jumper get out of such a relationship? The jumper receives synthetic strokes that feed the craving for affection. Such strokes are given in the form of attention, superficial praise, a shallow interest in the jumper's life, and a general acknowledgment that one does in fact exist. These are, of course, psychological scraps. But many oversocialized persons with a large Adapted Child are so stroke-hungry that they will gladly leap at psychological scraps.

We see clearly now why in so many instances "friends" want you to remain fat (although they would deny it). Your being fat contributes to your one-down position; you are easier to dominate. The person who relates to you out of a wish for power finds it easier to intimidate and control you when you are fat. The fat person is more childlike in appearance than the slim person; thus the fat person is more easily placed in the Child position.

KID FOODS

One of the ways in which your Child makes you fat is through the appeal of kid foods, foods such as hamburgers, hot dogs, French fries, potato chips, malts, sundaes, candy, doughnuts, and so forth. All these foods invoke the image of happy children having a good time at the circus or a ball game. When such foods are pictured, listed on menus, or presented to the eye, they activate your Child button. If your Adapted Child is particularly in need of strokes, these foods—unfortunately—tend to have a great deal of stroke value. We associate them with happy times and thus with happiness in general. When we are depressed, tense, bored—unhappy—the "happy foods" attract us.

As you know, such foods tend to be high in processed carbohydrates, refined sugar, and white flour. It is unfortunate that such foods are so widely advertised and promoted, in view of the fact that from a nutritional standpoint they supply mainly energy (and some vitamins and minerals), but *very little protein*. If you are fat, it is precisely the energy value of food that you *don't* need. The only way to lose weight is to burn off some of your stored fat in place of energy you would take in otherwise. On the other hand, you need protein to maintain the health of your tissues and body organs. Consequently, the kid foods are from a nutritional point of view the best foods to eliminate when you are seeking to reduce. So we have a double bind: The foods that are the best to eliminate in terms of Adult thinking are exactly the ones that appeal to our stroke-hungry Child.

There is no one Answer. There are answers. Each of us is an individual. Person A will find one way of coping with the appeal of kid foods and Person B will find another way. As we discuss in this chapter the topics of contacting your Child and coping with your Child, various principles allowing for freedom from the Child will emerge. However, for the present, let us say that the master principle, the one that underlies all the principles presented in this chapter or any other chapter, is *awareness*. In order to free yourself from self-destructive behavior patterns you need to have some understanding of what those patterns are, what sets them in motion, and what alternative responses are available to you.

Just the ability to look at certain foods and say to yourself, "Those are kid foods. They are pressing my Child button," is helpful. This very mental act introduces a certain amount of psychological distance between you and the food. It makes you less of a stimulus-response eating machine, and more of a human being.

EXCUSES

Children have a well-deserved reputation for making excuses. Their newly forming egos need protection, and they are not about to accept any blame for their actions if they can help it. To illustrate:

"Why did you get an 'F' on your spelling test, Billy?"

"I don't know. I guess Miss Jones hates me."

Similarly, your Child is no different from children all over the world. It does not want to be blamed for your being fat. Thus your Child will offer you a steady stream of excuses—good-sounding reasons, but not *real* reasons—for your overweight state. In Transactional Analysis an excuse is sometimes called a *wooden leg*. "Don't ask me to dance," says the person with a wooden leg. But we forget that there was a very famous dancer named Pegleg Pete who danced very well with a wooden leg. He danced *in spite of* his wooden leg. He had a wooden leg, but it didn't have him.

In Chapter One I touched upon some of the better-sounding excuses for being fat: blaming inborn body type, fat cells, defective carbohydrate metabolism, glandular problems, subtle brain injuries, and other complex biochemical-organic factors. The Child loves these high-sounding explanations for common, garden-variety obesity. They place the blame not on you, but on factors beyond your control.

There are many, many excuses that you can make for eating beyond your needs. And the Child may use any or all of them:

"I went to a birthday party. It was my little nephew's fourth birthday. And he would have been so disappointed if I didn't have some of his cake."

"I have to eat out with clients a lot. If I don't eat along with them, I'm not being sociable."

"We went to a big pot-luck picnic yesterday. There were so many tempting dishes that I just had to sample them."

"My mother invited us over for dinner last night. She's insulted if I don't have at least two helpings of everything."

"Candy is my downfall. My husband brought me two pounds of candy for Valentine's Day. I was on a strict diet, but he made me blow it."

"In the afternoon I just know my blood sugar gets too low from overwork. Nothing restores my energy like a candy bar or a soft drink."

"I have an irregular schedule—work a night shift as a nurse.

I can't plan regular meals, and I have to depend on snacks. So I can't help getting too many refined carbohydrates."

"I've been studying hard lately for my final exams, and when I'm studying I've just got to munch on something or I can't concentrate."

Well, it would be possible to go on and on. But you get the idea. The imaginative Child can invent excuses almost without limit. The idea is to blame something or someone else and to deny personal responsibility for your actions. This is the basic strategy underlying the excuses of the Child.

The aim of this section has been to alert you to the excuse-making tendencies of the Child. When you hear yourself mentally giving yourself a good-sounding reason for unnecessary eating or inappropriate choices, ask yourself, "Is this a real reason or an excuse? Am I saying that I have a wooden leg, and that I can't dance [i.e., lose weight] because of it?" These questions you are addressing to your Adult. Try to be sensitive to your Adult's answer. Possibly you will break out of a pattern of self-deception.

THE CHILD AND MAGIC

As you know, most children are delighted by magic tricks. Very young children really believe in magic. They think that rabbits actually pop out of empty hats, that heavy things can float in midair, and that objects can be made to disappear. Your Child retains its naïve belief in magic. There is a part of you that is fantasy-oriented, that believes wishing can make it so and that there are miraculous shortcuts to success in your endeavors.

It is for this reason that the overweight person is so often the victim of the charlatan and the quack. Weight control is big business in this country, and there are clever con artists lurking in all sorts of cunning disguises to take advantage of the gullible corpulent person.

When a person decides that he wants to lose weight, his impatient Child says, "I want the weight off *now.*" This starts the search for the Magic Shot, the Magic Pill, or the Magic Method that will make the fat disappear. Sometimes the search is for the Magician himself—the therapist, hypnotist, or Houdini who will rescue the person from himself. When I am counseling an overweight person, I want no part of the Child's search for magic. I prefer to relate to the client on an Adult-to-Adult basis, talk in rational terms, and refrain from making false promises or otherwise catering to the Child's illusions.

Do you remember Cinderella? Do you remember how she solved her problem of being unloved, unwanted, and rejected? Right. She didn't solve it herself. It was solved for her by her fairy godmother. Cinderella just waited around until somebody bailed her out, somebody with Powerful Magic. We have all heard too many fairy tales, and at a subconscious level—the Child level—we believe in them. The overweight person is often like Cinderella. He or she is waiting for somebody to come along and "make it all OK." Eric Berne used to refer to this kind of thinking as "waiting for Santa Claus."

Are you waiting for your fairy godmother, Santa Claus, or another magician to come into your life and change you from a fat frog into a slim prince or princess? Well, it's not going to happen. The Child is playing a fool's game. *There is no magic.* It's all up to you. And the sooner you realize it, the more likely you are to make some realistic plans about taking off your fat and keeping it off.

I have worked with hundreds of overweight people. I have heard about all kinds of shots and recently about the use of acupuncture for weight control. I am skeptical about the long-term benefits of most of the short-cut methods offered to the public. I have no doubt that under certain circumstances, with proper clinical evaluation, certain special treatments are of some benefit. Even acupuncture may prove to be of some value —it is too early to make a reliable evaluation. However, no treatment that works will be magic. All treatments that pro-duce permanent results will require in some degree the intelligent and responsible behavior of the person who seeks to lose weight. There is no way you can be a passive Cinderella and have it all done for you. To repeat: *There is no magic.*

The Child believes in magic. The Adult believes in rational action.

CONTACTING YOUR CHILD

In Chapter Two I suggested that you could make contact with your Parent ego state by asking yourself a set of reflective questions. The same strategy will be effective for contacting your Child. Again, I think it is useful to put your answers *in writing*. Here are some questions designed to help you contact your Child:

1. Do you tend to "go into" your Child often? What are some of the situations that push your Child button?

2. What are some of the feeling messages taped in your personal Child? What in particular makes you feel angry, anxious, bored, rejected, depressed, or unloved?

3. Do you sometimes go into your Child when you are in a particularly good mood? Under such conditions, do you tend to eat impulsively?

4. Which Child ego state seems to be the dominant one in you—the Adapted Child, the Rebellious Child, or the Natural Child?

5. Do you tend to "purchase" the affection of others by trying too hard to please them?

6. Do you feel you are suffering from a stroke hunger? Is much of your craving for food really your Child's hunger for strokes?

7. Can you think of a situation recently when your Little Professor pushed your Child button? Did the Child's reaction result in unnecessary eating?

8. Have you been hurt lately? Have you collected any brown stamps?

9. Have you done something particularly well lately? Have you collected any gold stamps?
10. Have you been trading in any stamps for "free" food?
11. When was the last time your Child bowed to the wish of a friend that you eat?
12. What are some of your favorite kid foods? Do you tend to turn to them when you feel in need of strokes?
13. What are some of your more frequently used excuses— wooden legs—for overeating or eating the wrong foods for you?
14. What is the central magical fantasy of your particular Child?

COPING WITH YOUR CHILD

Coping with your Child is no different in principle from coping with children in general. Children, as compared to psychologically mature adults, are more impulsive, emotional, demanding of attention, wayward, careless, and so forth. Wise adults cope with the ways of children through various practical strategies designed to socialize children without breaking their spirit. Similarly, the wise Adult in you can learn to cope with your troublesome Child in such a way as to help you lose weight without taking the joy out of life or eating. Below are some principles—general ones—worth considering. In the chapter titled "Using Your Adult to Lose Weight" I will be more specific. That chapter is designed to provide you with explicit management strategies for dealing with both your Parent and your Child.

1. Don't put down your Child. There is a tendency for the Parent to put down the Child when the Child falls below the standards of the Parent. Thus we are likely to engage in mental self-abuse. We may think such thoughts as: "You fool! Why did you go back to the buffet table for seconds?"

or "You're nothing but a hopeless slob!" or "You're never going to lose weight. You don't have any will power." These are all messages from the Controlling Parent to the Child. They will make the Child feel bad, and feeling bad is one of the causes of overeating. Instead, from your intelligent Adult, criticize your behavior. You can say to yourself, "I shouldn't have taken a second piece of pie. I've got to work out some practical strategies for coping with social situations that induce me to eat beyond my needs." This sort of thought reveals a *problem-solving* approach as opposed to a blaming approach, and is consequently of some value.

2. When you find yourself slipping into a Child ego state, ask yourself, "Do I really want to allow myself to slip into my Child now?" There are numerous ways of staying in your Adult. To illustrate, when confronted with a tempting dessert you can ask yourself, "Would I feel deprived if I passed it by?" You may be surprised to hear the answer in your head: "I wouldn't feel deprived." The temptation often comes more from the sight and smell of food, the fact that food is being advertised or offered, the way food is displayed and served, or from your being part of a social situation in which others are eating, than it does from your deeper desires. The Child, of course, is very suggestible, and it responds to superficial appeals. Eating under such conditions we can designate as *stimulus-induced eating,* eating that does not arise from physical hunger or even stroke hunger, but the invitational characteristics of food.

3. Stroke your Child when it behaves in a responsible manner. For example, if at a meal you take only a small helping of a starchy food, tell yourself, "That was all right. You did what you said you were going to do, and that's the way you'll succeed in the long run." This is a good, positive form of self-stroking. However, don't be too lavish in your self-praise. Praise your actions, not your character. If you are too general in your self-praise, you may build up an unreal-

istic self-image about your capacity to eat properly. Then, a small deviation may make you feel terribly guilty, terribly disappointed in yourself, and you will be setting yourself up for a binge. Binges tend to arise from a vicious circle in which you pound on your Child for cheating, then feel guilty and depressed, crave strokes as a consequence, eat because of the stroke hunger, then pound on your Child for eating, then feel guilty and depressed, and so forth. If you stroke yourself for your actions, not for your wonderful character, you are less likely to set up the preconditions for binge eating.

4. Be aware that your Child's behavior has a purpose. For most of you reading this book, a key problem is the stroke hunger of your Adapted Child. The Adapted Child uses food as a form of self-stroking. When it feels bored, anxious, unloved, rejected, or tense, the Child turns to food for synthetic gratification. I sometimes say to overweight people, "You are looking for something in the food that isn't there." Work on contacting your Child and thus knowing the purpose or purposes of its eating behavior. Ask yourself, "What is it my Child really wants? How can I get it without eating?" If you get to know your own Child, you can eventually find ways of satisfying more and more of its purposes without food.

5. Give your Child a choice. Don't allow your Controlling Parent to force the Child into submission. The Child will only rebel in time if you do that. Don't say to yourself, "No soft drinks for you! Only water!" Instead say, "I don't think a soft drink with sugar would be wise. But how about an artificially sweetened drink?" Don't say, "No more between-meal eating. You can't handle it." Say instead, "It's all right to eat something between meals if you plan it as part of your total intake and if it's low in calories." Don't say, "You're never going to eat ice cream again!" Say instead, "You can have ice cream in moderation. Let's set up a concept of how much and how often would be appropri-

ate." Listen to your Child and let it have a say in the matter. Don't let the Child take over, but don't stifle it entirely either.

6. Get in the habit of using your intelligent Adult to orient your Child toward reality. When you are going through an internal conflict or making a difficult decision, the ego states are sending messages back and forth. Try to make the messages to your Child come from a reasonable Adult that respects the Child, not from a Critical Parent that mocks the Child's feelings.

The art of coping with your Child can be acquired. It is a skill like any other skill, and similar in kind to the communication skills used by effective parents. You will succeed in coping with your Child and in losing weight if you keep in the front of your mind the thought that you must *guide* your Child, not coerce it.

4

How the Food Industry
Appeals to the Child

The child you once were does not die when you become an adult. That child is incorporated into your adult personality and emerges from time to time, influencing you to make impulsive decisions based on short-term pleasures opposed to your long-term welfare. The food industry and the advertising agencies it employs to promote its products know this well. A tremendous amount of today's advertising is based on emotional appeals, appeals aimed at your Child. These appeals often lead you to act contrary to your rational self, or your Adult. Becoming more aware of how the food industry appeals to your Child will help you succeed in your struggle against unwanted fat and unnecessary eating.

In its advertising and packaging, the food industry presents information to your senses that leads to what I call *stimulus-induced eating*. Stimulus-induced eating is eating that takes place in response to certain invitational characteristics associated with food, not to an inner state of actual hunger. (Thus the old advertising advice that the copywriter should "Sell the sizzle, not the steak.") For example, suppose you are watching television after dinner. You are not hungry or thinking of food. Suddenly a child appears on the screen eating a candy bar. As he takes a bite, a look of ecstasy appears on his face. "It's yummy!" he says directly to you. If you are suggestible, you may find yourself wishing that you had a yummy candy bar too. The child in the advertisement has appealed directly to your Child ego state, activating it, and thus leading you to want to eat when you did not want to eat a moment ago. This is all rather obvious when we think about it in this way. Unfortunately, it is not so obvious when we are involved in the situation. Like the fish that does not know it is in the water, you do not always know that your Child is under the influence of external stimuli.

In this chapter, let us examine some of the specific ways in which the food industry appeals to your Child. By becoming aware of these appeals, your Adult self can stand back and say, "So that's what they're doing! Well, I'm not going to let them hook my Child that way! I'm a grownup now, not a baby. And I can think for myself. I don't need an advertising agency or a food franchise chain to do my thinking for me."

MAGAZINE PROMOTION

Most of the magazine advertisements for food are found in one kind of magazine, the women's slicks. The women's slicks contain articles on such subjects as child-rearing, decorating, communication in marriage, and, of course, food. They are to be contrasted with women's pulp magazines, which specialize in confession stories or the vagaries of the lives of movie stars. The men's magazines, whether slick or pulp, do not contain a large number of food ads. Let us concentrate then on the women's slicks, and the kind of messages they beam out to their readers.

I have before me a copy of a typical women's slick. The cover of the magazine shows in full color a picture of a fancy dessert, and inside the magazine there is an article on how to make it. How delighted a woman's husband and children will be with the dessert! The children will hug her and kiss her. The husband will give her an appreciative peck on the cheek. Such words as "tasty," "scrumptious," and "delicious" are used to describe the dessert itself. The whole presentation is aimed at the Child of Mrs. Typical Homemaker. It is designed in part to allay her fears about being a competent homemaker: "Am I a good cook? Can I make my family happy with food? Am I as good in the kitchen as the woman next door?" It is implied that the answer to all these questions will be a resounding "Yes!" if she follows the recipes recommended by her favorite women's magazine.

As we look through the magazine, however, we find that the reader's Child is bombarded with conflicting messages. The magazine quite typically contains an article on dieting. Almost every issue of every women's slick contains at least one article on how to lose weight. In such articles one finds no delicious desserts. On the contrary, the dieter is faced with a bleak landscape of cottage cheese, salad with lemon juice, and black coffee. The implied message now becomes: "If you want to be slim and beautiful, if you want to be appealing to your man, if you want to look trim in your bathing suit this summer, if you don't want your husband to have an affair, then *diet* and *suffer!*" Thus the *same* magazine sends to the *same* reader a set of *double-bind messages,* messages that say "Do" and "Don't" at the same time.

The hapless homemaker is told that she should fix rich desserts for her family, playing the role of Old-Fashioned Mama. At the same time she is told that she should be slim and beautiful, playing the role of Beauty Queen or Showgirl for her husband. Is it thus implied that she would pass up the tasty treats she fixes? Or is it implied that by some sort of metabolic magic she can eat desserts whenever she likes and still be thin? If you just happen to be the homemaker in question, you must learn to sort out double-bind messages. Say to yourself, "These are double-bind messages! First they say 'Do' and then they say 'Don't.' First they say 'Goody-goody' and they they say 'Naughty-naughty.' First they say I should and then they say I shouldn't. Well, I don't have to take orders from a magazine. I have my own mind, and I'll use it!"

Like most women's magazines, the one before me has a full-page ad for a product that will help an overweight woman lose weight quickly and easily. Before and after pictures show a depressed fat woman "before" and a smiling slim woman "after." This ad is also an appeal to the Child at several levels. The psychological messages from the ad to the Child are: (1) "Fat is bad. You will be depressed and unhappy if you are fat." (2) "Yes, Virginia, there is a Santa Claus. The world does have magic in it. Our special pill, shot, method, or device works like the wand wielded by Cinderella's fairy godmother. With no particular effort on your part, it can change you from the gray drudge you are now into Miss Radiant Sunshine!" (3) "No, sweetheart, you don't have to wait for a long time for the transformation to occur. Didn't you know that miracles take place overnight? Almost before you can say 'Metamorphosis!' you'll be the lovely person that Mother Nature intended you to be!"

Learn to look at such ads with a cynical eye. Say to yourself, "The ad is psychological nonsense. There is no magic in the domain of weight control. Yes, I can be slim. But it will require thought and applied intelligence on my part. I can get slim and stay slim by using my rational Adult, not by listening to appeals directed at my irrational Child."

Let us now turn to food ads in the women's slicks. Again, studying the typical magazine before me can be instructive. I made a tally of the number of ads for food it contained. Out of about one hundred ads, somewhat more than thirty were for foods of various kinds. In other words, approximately one-third of the advertising space was devoted to food! Keep in mind that the non-food ads included a broad spectrum of products ranging from children's clothes to books to pain relievers to hair colorings to sanitary pads to detergents. It would seem that an inordinate amount of space in such magazines is devoted to telling us what to eat, particularly in view of the fact that we would eat anyway—advertising or no advertising.

I also made an analysis of the prepared products versus the non-prepared products. There were only three ads for foods in their natural states: one for potatoes, a second for bananas, and a third for pineapple. All the rest of the ads were for canned foods, boxed foods, bottled baby foods, bottled sauces, boxed dinners, and so forth. These foods were characterized as "quick," "easy," or "instant." This emphasis on ease of preparation appeals to the inner Child, to the emotional desire to have things accomplished with a minimum of effort. The impatient Child wants it *now*. And the mass merchandiser of food takes advantage of our impatient tendencies.

Another obvious appeal to the Child used in the ads is in the words chosen to describe the products. There is very little real information about nutritional value, protein content, caloric content, vitamin and mineral content. Nothing is said about artificial food colorings, artificial food flavorings, and other additives to processed foods. As you know, this is information that will appear only in fine print on the container. Why? This is data for your thinking Adult, and products are not sold by giving the Adult information. The words used to describe the products are almost all words with an emotional appeal, words directed at your Child. Here are some of the words and phrases used in the food ads of the typical women's magazine I have been studying: *snack, country, luscious, treat, something special, crunchy, tempting, creamy, fantastic flavor, sensational taste, gourmet, simmer, seasonings, tender, stuffed, rich, delicious, savory, smooth, terrific taste, fantastic taste, great taste, delicate flavor, old-fashioned,* and *home-style.* Although the words are taken out of context, their Child appeal remains. It is clear that such words convey no real information. They are used in ads to sell products by appealing to old emotional tapes recorded by you in childhood.

In looking through the typical women's magazine, I noticed another way advertisers try to appeal to your Child—by the use of Nurturing Parent figures. These symbolical figures are rather obviously mothers, aunts, and grandmothers, and they are recommending from their old-fashioned farmlike kitchens such products as bottled foods and boxed dinners. The idea, of course, is to convey a feeling of love and warmth in association with the advertised product. Our best strokes come from the Nurturing Parent ego state of an actual adult, and your inner Child is supposed to think in response to the ad something like this: "Mom gave me love. Mom gave me food. Therefore food is love. The mom in this ad looks warm and kindly like my Mom. If I eat Mother Nostalgia's Old-Fashioned Southern Rice Boxed Dinner, I will fill my being with love." Now, as ridiculous as this seems, the Child is capable of this kind of unrealistic logic. Be aware of the illogical tendencies of your Child. When confronted with ads utilizing Nurturing Parent figures, say to yourself, "Food is *not* love. My Child often tends to confuse the two. And the mother in this ad is not my Mom. This is a photograph of a model pretending to be a mother. And the old-fashioned kitchen is a stage set." These realistic thoughts from your Adult will block uncritical acceptance by your Child.

TELEVISION ADVERTISING

It has been estimated that the average adult in this country watches as many as 4,000 television commercials a year! If this figure sounds too large to you, let's break it down. Assume that you watch an hour of television. You will probably see about six commercials during this time. That may even be a conservative figure. If you were to watch an average of three hours a day, that would be eighteen commercials a day. Multiply 18 by 365, the number of days in a year, and the product is 6,570—substantially more than 4,000. It is easy to believe that many adults are exposed to 4,000 or more television commercials a year.

It would not seem unreasonable to estimate that about one-fourth of these TV ads have to do with food or drink. Ads for candy bars, soft drinks, hot dogs, crackers, potato chips, ice cream, and chains of franchise restaurants are presented throughout the viewing hours. So if you are a typical television watcher, it is quite possible that you see as many as 1,000 commercials a year telling you what to eat and where to eat it.

Perhaps you are one of those people who say, "Oh, the commercials don't affect me. I ignore them." However, there may be times when you watch commercials in a state of passive attention resembling a hypnotic trance. Under such conditions, you are very suggestible. The commercial message bypasses your Adult and reaches your Child. This is so because you are not watching with all your critical faculties. Your Child is being programmed to accept the ideas and advice presented. If, however, you watch a commercial with active attention, you can then say to yourself, "How obvious! Do they think I'm that dumb? What a blatant appeal to my Child!" One of my successful weight-control clients told me that she talks back—out loud —to television commercials! This represents a dramatic rejection by her Adult of the messages aimed at her Child.

If you think you are unaffected by the food ads on television, consider the fact that millions of dollars are being spent to influence somebody. If advertising is not affecting you, then it is certainly having some impact on the person next door. On the other hand, from the point of view of the person next door, *you* are the person next door!

One of the principal ways TV commercials are made to appeal to your Child is by the use of actual children. A large percentage of commercials show children doing cute things, running, laughing, playing, and singing, all in association with the food or drink being ballyhooed. The psychological message is: "The fun, the joy, the spontaneity of childhood can be recaptured by eating our product."

Often in the commercials you will see an adult joining the happy child. The adult wants some of the food too! Sometimes he even steals it from the child. A struggle may follow. Usually there is some sort of happy truce in which adult and child are shown joyfully eating together. If you look closely at the commercials showing an adult eating in the presence of a child, you will usually see that the adult has regressed! His face, his body language, his entire being, convey that he has temporarily *become* a child again! This is precisely what TA means by "entering an ego state," in this case the ego state of the Child. The psychological message is: "You can become a kid again."

The famous child psychologist Jean Piaget made it amply evident through his research on thinking processes that from about the age of two to seven children perceive the world in primarily *anthropomorphic* and *animistic* terms. The word "anthropomorphic" means having the form and structure of man. (Note the resemblance to the word "anthropology.") Anthropomorphic thinking is thinking that explains aspects of nature in terms of human characteristics. For example, we might speak of Mr. Sun, Mr. Wind, Father Time, Jack Frost, and so forth. The word "animistic" is closely related. It refers to things having a life, a spirit, or a soul. Thus children may think that Mr. Sun is happy, Mr. Wind is restless, or that Father Time is bored. Primitive people believe that the trees, the rocks, the river, and other inanimate objects in their environment possess souls. Similarly, the modern child, going through the magical stage of thought, thinks that the world of natural processes and physical things has the same feelings and motives as human beings and living things.

What does all this have to do with television advertising? The fact is, TV commercials are often designed to appeal to the residual anthropomorphic and animistic tendencies in your own Child. The Child in you thinks much like the little being you were during your early childhood. Appealing to your Child, the food ads make remarkable use of anthropomorphic and animistic thinking. Many of them are filled with talking animals, talking objects, and talking foods. They dance, prance, and sing, extolling the joys to be had by purchasing and eating the food or drink in question. The idea is for the ad to bypass your analytical Adult and to appeal directly to your nonanalytical Child. If you are susceptible—and most of us are to some degree —you will be captivated by the charm of the ad. Again, under such conditions you are more responsive to psychological messages.

Closely connected with the anthropomorphic and animistic themes are all the symbolical figures of early childhood. The magician, the clown, the puppet, the doll, the toy soldier, the rocking horse, and the stuffed animal are examples of such symbolical figures. During your adulthood you will find them still at work on television, telling you that you can return to the joys of childhood by eating certain foods or eating at certain franchise chains.

Although many such commercials are intended for children, a large number appear on prime time, when the principal viewers are adults. Study them carefully with your logical Adult, and you will see quite clearly the ways in which they appeal to your Child. Often adults will be shown eating with the happy faces of young children. The message of the food industry on television seems to be: "Happiness is eating what we are selling." You can counteract this message to some extent by saying to yourself from your Adult, "Happiness is not food, and food is not happiness. I can't find something in food that isn't there."

COFFEE SHOPS SELL MORE THAN COFFEE

Coffee shops quite obviously sell more than coffee. They could just as well be called hamburger shops, malt shops, ice cream shops, pie shops, or cake shops. The modern well-designed air-conditioned coffee shop is a wonder of merchandising. I'm not speaking of a mom-and-pop café on the side of an old boulevard; I'm speaking of a place to be found on a freeway or highway—a place where a bit of money has been spent, where there is an investment in psychological appeal. Study such places, and you will find many ways in which they speak to your Child.

Let us pay an imaginary visit to one such coffee shop—a composite of many coffee shops I have been to. Driving into the parking lot, we see the name of the shop. It is part of a franchise chain, and the name suggests a circus clown. As we enter, there is the unmistakable atmosphere of a circus. It is subdued, not blatant at all. This is not one of your "cheap" coffee shops. The happy mood is created, but also a relaxed let's-stay-awhile mood. This too is designed to appeal to the Child, the very young Child in you. The psychological message is: "Trust me." Thoughts go through your head like: "What a nice place! I just like being here. I've got to come back and bring the kids. They'll really enjoy it. Oh, and look at that! Every table has a miniature cut-out three-dimensional carrousel that is also the menu. Isn't that cute!"

After we are seated, the waitress comes to our table. She is young and pretty and personable. She wears a button with a happy face. It says, "I like you. Have a nice day." (Stroke, stroke.) The first thing she says, and pleasantly, is, "Before you order, can I bring anyone coffee?" (Stroke.) In keeping with the circus atmosphere, the waitress is dressed in leotards and a short skirt. As we look around, we see that all the waitresses are cute and young.

We look at the menu. It is several pages in length, containing a number of full-color photographs of various foods and desserts. Who looks at picture books? You guessed it—children. The illustrated menu is designed to appeal directly to your Child. There you see before you in glorious, almost three-dimensional color the hamburgers, the hot dogs, the fried chicken, the fries, the shakes, the pies, the cakes, the donuts, and the sundaes. I remember when many coffee shops had only typed or mimeographed menus. The printed menu was a step forward. But the glossy illustrated menu is a quantum leap for psychological marketing. Pictures appeal directly to the Child. They make a powerful nonverbal suggestion to purchase and eat the food. If, for example, you are trying to restrict carbohydrates this week, looking at a beautiful photograph of a hot fudge sundae with white whipped cream topped with chopped nuts and a glossy candied cherry can hardly work in favor of your original decision.

Taking advantage of the state of the Child, when it is dessert time the waitress does not ask, "Would you like dessert today?" No, instead she asks, "What kind of dessert would you like today?" She has obviously been instructed in the art of sales-manship. The second question utilizes a psychological strategy called *implied consent.* In other words, it is taken for granted that you have already decided to eat a dessert. If your already tempted Child is placed in this position, you are likely to suc-cumb to the moment's desire. Knowing the principle involved can be helpful. You can say to yourself, from your Adult, "She's using implied consent on me. And I rather resent that kind of blatant manipulation."

As we walk to the register with the check, we notice a sign on it: "It was fun to serve you. Hope you had a good time." (Stroke, stroke.) The manager takes our money and encourages each of us to take a lollipop from a container close at hand. As we leave, sucking our lollipops, we feel a kind of a happy glow. It's no wonder. The whole experience has been like a short time-machine trip back to childhood. The Child feels stroked and is purring cozily. We will want to come back here again.

TAKE-OUT CHAINS

The take-out chains and the coffee shops have much in com-mon. Indeed, coffee shops are often part of a chain operated either by a parent corporation or franchise holders. However, I am presently thinking of the short-order take-out franchise chains that specialize in hamburgers, fries, hot dogs, shakes, and a few desserts. The growth of these establishments has been phenomenal in the past few years. It is not at all unusual for relatively small towns to have four or five take-out places. They are centers of activity. It's where the gang goes. It's also where the family goes. Here Mom and Dad and several kids can have a relatively inexpensive weekday evening or Sunday afternoon outing.

The take-out places have undergone a substantial evolution

over the years. In the past, you had to wait in line for your food and eat it in the car. Now quite a few of these establishments have air-conditioned dining rooms. You still wait in line to give your order, but you sit down and eat it in substantial comfort. A number of the outlets have evolved even further; your order is brought to your table on a tray. This, of course, transforms the original take-out establishment into an eat-in place not unlike the coffee shop. The added comforts are all in the direction of giving more strokes to your Child. The more you are catered to, the more that is done for you, the more your Child feels that someone out there *cares.*

The take-out shop tends to be even more blatant in its appeal to the Child than the typical coffee shop. At many of these outlets we find a vast array of offerings from the world of childhood: balloons, comic books, funny hats, whistles, pencil mazes, and so forth. The décor favors dolls, puppets, clowns, animals, and cowboys. And many of the food items have names based on words like "yummy," "super," and "whopper." Children are obviously their stock in trade. Without children, they could not succeed.

However, what may be less obvious is that the trinkets and animated characters also push your Child button. If you're susceptible, you may find yourself rather quickly in a Child ego state. Indeed, the latent wish to enter the Child ego state may be one of the reasons that many parents take the initiative and suggest to their children that they all stop in at a franchise outlet. Once you are in the Child ego state, you are much more apt to eat carelessly. Rationalizations such as, "The Super Shake and the Yummyburger with the fries isn't going to hurt me just this once," are more likely to occur. Learn to say instead from your Adult, "All these toys and talking animals are pushing my Child button. But I have a choice. I can decide to behave out of my responsible Adult."

By the way, I am not saying that you can't enjoy yourself. If you stay in your Adult, you can let your Child play in a modified manner. When I go to a franchise outlet with my family, I have coffee or sugar-free cola instead of a shake. We get one order of fries and share it, thus teaching ourselves and our son that it is OK to eat fries, but it is also possible to eat them in moderation. I often eat my hamburger open face, thereby cutting the carbohydrate intake from the bread in half. My method of eating at a franchise outlet allows me to participate in a family activity, does not overly deprive my Child, and at the same time keeps the calorie and/or carbohydrate count to one-half what it might have been. I have encouraged my overweight clients to use similar methods, with good results. Try to eliminate the either-or kind of thinking that says, "Either you go to franchise outlets and stuff yourself or you stay away from them." As I said in Chapter Three, you must learn to make intelligent compromises with your Child. Don't repress the Child with your Controlling Parent. Instead work *with* the Child, using your reality-oriented Adult.

WINE AND DINE

And what about the better restaurants? What about the kinds of places that a husband takes his wife on a special occasion, the places that appeal to couples seeking a romantic atmosphere? Do they cater to your Child? Of course they do. For one thing, the waiter suggests that you have one or two drinks before dinner. This in itself encourages regression to a more infantile level of functioning. He calls you Sir or Miss or Ma'am, building up your sense of importance. The more attentive he is, the more stroke value for your Child his behavior has. Let us say that he brings a tray of hot cheese bread wrapped in a linen napkin. He elaborately unfolds it, offering a slice first to the woman, then to the man. Is all this service necessary? Can't you pass your own bread and take it off a tray yourself? Of course you can. Just last night you ate at a take-out place and carried your own tray to the table. The extra service is obviously given as part of the art of merchandising. It has tremendous stroke value. Whenever anyone pays attention to you, treats you as if you are important, and caters to your wishes, that person cannot help stroking your Child. The professional waiter who knows how to stroke your Child is actually playing the role of Nurturing Parent. Unfortunately, the fine art of waiting tables in the European style is declining in the United States. But perhaps you should be grateful. Poor service snaps you back to reality, and your Adult is in charge of your eating decisions!

The darkness, the coziness, the cavelike atmosphere of many better restaurants, unconsciously suggest a prenatal environment, again encouraging regression. As your Adult recedes under the impact of the dim environment, the before-dinner drinks, the wine with dinner, and the attentions of the waiter, your vigilance and your concern with calories and carbohydrates undergoes a parallel recession. The impulsive Child emerges, and it is easy to eat a second and a third piece of cheese bread, the whole baked potato, and a rich dessert.

Dessert is particularly appealing to the Child. In some restaurants a tray is wheeled out with a spectacular array of French pastries, tarts, cheesecake slices, and other goodies. It is difficult to resist something when it is right before your eyes. Very young children do not think in abstract terms. The concrete presentation of a dessert is a direct appeal to the very young Child in you. Desserts can even be utilized as entertainment pieces. One restaurant I know of specializes in an ice cream sundae that is made to look like a South Seas volcanic island. A crouton soaked in brandy is lit by the waiter. The flame leaps up, and one can imagine that the sauce is lava. The whole thing is quite delightful, and the Child is tempted to order the dessert just so it won't miss out on any of the evening's fun.

SUPERMARKETING IN THE SUPERMARKETS

Let's take a walk together through a typical supermarket and take note of some of the ways in which foods and drinks are displayed to enhance their appeal to the Child. One of the first things we notice is that a very small percentage of the floor space is devoted to unprocessed foods. Meats, dairy products, and produce are located along the walls. Some of the center aisles are devoted to household-maintenance items such as detergents, paper towels, trash bags, and the like. Perhaps two-thirds of the center aisles are given over to foods and drinks, bottled, canned, boxed, and frozen. Processed foods dominate the scene. If you like refined carbohydrates, you will find them in abundance here in various cereal products, snack foods, and frozen desserts.

We note that one aisle has a large display of candy. As if that is not enough, we find candy displayed again in another place in the store. And now we see that there is also a candy rack at every check-out stand. The idea here is that as your Child becomes bored and restless standing in line, you are likely to indulge in an impulsive purchase.

One of the messages being sent to your Child by the vast arrays of frozen and boxed dinners labeled "instant" is that life can be a snap, a breeze, a lot of fun. Who wants to work and actually *cook* food in a hot kitchen when there are so many other things to do in this world?

The names of the products are chosen to appeal to the Child. There are many references to storybook or fairy tale characters, nursery rhymes, famous children's songs, and the whole fantasy life of early childhood. An appeal to a better way of life—when humankind was in its own childhood—is made by the frequent use of words like "farm," "country," "nature," "garden," "kitchen," and so forth. The aim is to induce a state of nostalgia, to bring to mind images of barefoot children playing by the old swimmin' hole or running through meadows with their dogs. To the Child of the city dweller, such images make a strong appeal. At an unconscious level, we almost believe that buying and eating these products can send us back in time to a better world.

We see the words "high protein" in big letters on a number

of boxes. But wait a moment. Reading the fine print on the container, we see that the item in question is only 16 percent protein. The carbohydrate content is 61 percent, and the fat content 23 percent. Apparently the words "high protein" in this case merely mean that this item has more protein than most wheat-based or grain-based products. Our Child was attracted to the big letters on the box, but it was our Adult who read the fine print. This does not always happen.

Overhead we spot a moving display. A mechanical cardboard bear on a unicycle is cleverly balanced on a high wire. He pedals furiously back and forth, two large sugar-cereal boxes dangling from the ends of his balance pole. We stop and watch for a while, wondering what marvel of mechanical engineering keeps the mechanical bear from falling. The whole display is delightful to the Child in several ways: It moves, it is big, and it has a cheerful animated animal. We cannot help feeling good about the product associated with the display.

Now we come to a spectacular array of potato chips. The large amount of space devoted to this particular product is really quite surprising. There are several brands, various kinds of new containers, new flavors, new shapes, new sizes. The marketing concept here is novelty. Although people obviously like potato chips and buy them, they tend to get bored with the same old thing. The wide variety of products appeals to the Child's wish for something different. Confronted with a new flavor or a new shape, the Child reacts with, "Gee, I wonder what that's like?" And you are on your way to another impulsive purchase.

And here are the wines. There are many different flavors, names, and bottle shapes—again the theme is novelty. One of the favorite merchandising devices here is to associate wines with faraway places, with South Sea islands or regions in Spain or Italy. Here we have an appeal to the Child's wanderlust, with the feeling of being bored and restless at home. At an unconscious level the labels suggest escape from the tedium of everyday living.

Yes, the supermarket is a marvel of modern merchandising —a far cry from the general store of the past. (Interestingly enough, as we have seen, the old-fashioned images are sometimes invoked by the pictures and titles on the containers.) The goal of all of the clever packaging, copywriting, and artwork is to bypass your analytical Adult and appeal directly to your uncritical Child.

There are several ways in which you can buttress your Adult and reduce the likelihood of behaving and buying out of your Child.

1. Go into the supermarket with a shopping list, determined to buy only the items on the list. This will discourage impulsive purchases.

2. Don't go into the supermarket hungry. When you are hungry, your Child is just that much more suggestible.

3. When you are wavering about a purchase, make a conscious decision to enter your Adult ego state. Ask yourself, "What would my Adult say about this purchase? Is it something I really want? Would I feel cheated driving home in the car knowing I passed up this item?" Again, this is not to say that you can never have treats, snacks, carbohydrate foods, wines, etc. To take that approach would be to repress your Child with your Controlling Parent, and I'm against that. It will only backfire in the long run. On the other hand, if you listen only to the Child, you will buy a new item before a similar item at home is used up. Your Adult will help you to make a reasonable compromise between the Controlling Parent and the Child. Say to yourself from your Adult, "OK, we'll try the new potato chips, but not until the old ones at home are gone. Next week is soon enough to try the new ones. And we'll buy a small bag instead of a big one so we can see if we really like them."

BREAKFAST CEREALS

Breakfast cereals particularly are packaged and promoted in ways that appeal to children. Once again we see the parade of clowns, cartoon characters, monsters, and cowboys. The packages often include toys and trinkets. And again, these advertising devices may also appeal to your Child.

Cereal boxes convey the impression of being relatively large containers because the vertical and horizontal dimensions are emphasized. The third dimension, the depth, is seen only when the box is turned sideways. A relatively large-appearing cereal box with dimensions of 10 inches by 8 inches by 2 inches contains about 160 cubic inches. If the same volume were to be enclosed in a cube with equal sides, the box would be about 5.5 inches by 5.5 inches by 5.5 inches, and it would look rather small. Obviously, smart marketing takes advantage of optical illusions. The suggestible Child sees only the superficial bigness of the container. It takes the analytical Adult to visualize the container as a cube, and this is obviously seldom done.

Returning once more to the words "high protein," what do they mean when applied to breakfast cereals? Again, "high protein" merely indicates that the cereal in question has more protein than most other cereals, not that its main ingredient is protein. A typical high-protein cereal contains about 22 percent protein and 78 percent carbohydrate. In contrast, a typical whole-wheat cereal contains 11 percent protein, 85 percent carbohydrate, and 4 percent fat. Of course, even the whole-wheat cereal is a "high-protein" cereal when compared with a sugar cereal. A typical sugar cereal contains about 8 percent protein and 92 percent carbohydrate. The principal source of protein in a sugar-cereal breakfast is in the milk that is poured over it!

If you like sugar cereals, and your children like them, and you want to cut down on their consumption, what should be done?

Should you eliminate them from the family diet completely? Fine, if there are no repercussions from your Child or your family. If your Child, your children, or your spouse protest too vehemently, a compromise is possible. For example, have only one sugar cereal in your pantry at a time and allow yourself or your children to eat it one morning a week as a special treat. If the adults in the family don't care for sugar cereals, and if you have only one child, your problem is easily solved. Allow the child to make the selection of the sugar cereal, again permitting only one box in the house at a time. If there are two or more members in the family who like sugar cereals, the choice can be a revolving responsibility. A democratic attitude is fostered by giving children voices in such decisions. They will not develop hang-ups about sugar foods if these foods are allowed in moderate quantities.

THE MANIPULATED PERSON

It is well for you to remind yourself that this is the Age of Supersell. With rising personal wealth and a multitude of products to sell, big corporations have become increasingly interested in the psychology of advertising. As economist John Kenneth Galbraith says in *The Affluent Society:*

> . . . many of the desires of the individual are no longer evident to him. They become so only as they are synthesized, elaborated and nurtured by advertising and salesmanship, and these, in turn, have become among our most important and talented professions. Few people at the beginning of the nineteenth century needed an adman to tell them what they wanted.*

The adman in the food industry *creates* desires for certain products. This leads to stimulus-induced behavior, including buying and eating, a form of behavior that is determined *not*

*John K. Galbraith, *The Affluent Society* (Paperback: New American Library, 1959), p. 30.

by inner needs but by manufactured wishes. In the language of TA, the adman finds ways to appeal to your nonvigilant Child.

It is to your advantage to look at all this out of the eyes of your Adult. Think: "If I am overly suggestible, if my Child is too easily reached, I am allowing myself to be manipulated. But I'm not a child anymore. I'm a grownup, an adult, and I can decide for myself. I don't need an adman to play the role of Controlling Parent, telling me what to do."

SPELL-BREAKING IN THE TWENTIETH CENTURY

Research conducted by experimental psychologists on the perceptions of overweight persons clearly demonstrates that as a group they tend to be spellbound by food. Their behavior is dominated by stimuli associated with food. The food industry capitalizes on these suggestible tendencies of the chronic over-eater. However, spell-breaking in the twentieth century is possible. You don't have to behave out of an entranced Child. You can learn to enter your Adult ego state at will, making intelligent decisions about buying and eating.

I hope that this chapter has been a consciousness-raising experience for you. The simple fact that you now have a clearer understanding of how the food industry appeals to your Child should contribute to placing the buying and eating of food under the greater control of your Adult. Anything you can do to increase self-awareness will be helpful. The following psychological exercises will help you strengthen your Adult and break out of the spell of stimulus-induced eating:

1. Find a food ad in one of the women's slicks. Does it make a direct appeal to your Child? If so, how?
2. For a few hours some evening, watch one TV channel and keep a count on paper of the number of food versus non-food commercials. How many of the commercials are for snack foods and processed foods? Were children used in

the ads? Did the adults in the ads often act like children? Were there many giants, storybook characters, talking animals, and the like?

3. The next time you are in a coffee shop take special notice of the various ways it appeals to your emotional nature. What kind of atmosphere or mood is created? Is there a special theme: Gay Nineties, ragtime, down-on-the-farm? If so, how does the theme contribute to stimulus-induced eating?

4. Stop in at a take-out place when you are not hungry and without any children. Order just a cup of coffee or a sugar-free drink. Then study the signs and the décor in your Adult ego state. Make yourself aware of all the ways in which the outlet appeals to the Child ego state.

5. When you are eating dinner at a better restaurant, take note of the subtle ways in which regression is encouraged. Observe how a skillful waiter builds up your sense of importance.

6. Walk down the aisles of a supermarket with a notebook and a pencil, listing at random all the ways your Child is stimulated. If you actually try this experiment, you will be surprised at how rapidly the list will grow. The examples I gave earlier in the chapter are only a few of the possible messages aimed at your child. You can increase your awareness substantially by finding your own.

7. While you are in the supermarket, take a look at the breakfast cereal display. Count the number of modified cereals versus unprocessed cereals. Take note of the many ways in which the packages appeal to children. Read the fine print on the sides of the boxes and be aware of the many cereals containing a great deal of sugar, artificial flavors, and other additives. Also, compare the protein, carbohydrate, and fat content of a number of cereals.

If you are overweight, and if stimulus-induced eating has anything to do with it, don't waste your time blaming the food industry. It is just one more cop-out on your part to say, "It's all big business. It's the way they appeal to my Child. If they would change their ways, I could lose weight." Even if such rationalizations are "right" in some abstract sense, they won't do you any good. Indulging yourself in them is just playing a futile blaming game. Throughout history people in business have been marketing their wares. Salesmanship is an ancient art and, as we have already noted, in an age of affluence the skills associated with it are of great importance.

No, don't play the blaming game. The only answer is to face the reality of the situation and to accept the responsibility for your behavior. This your Child will not do. You must do it with your Adult. I have shown you in this chapter many ways in which you can move into your Adult ego state when you are stimulated to eat. Take advantage of them, and under the guidance of your rational Adult become the slim person nature intended you to be.

5

The Life Positions and the Overweight Person

The other day in my TA weight-control class I gave the group the following assignment: "Briefly state in writing how you feel about yourself in terms of inferiority and/or superiority in relation to other people in general." Here is the response of Mildred C.:

Mother never could be pleased. I was too skinny as a child. She felt my hair was too stringy, and she cut it like a boy's. I talked too fast—had early problems with stuttering. Later in high school I stammered some. I felt very inferior.

As a mature adult I feel I function well, am sharp and able to do a good job. I do seem to have a too high drive behavior pattern. I overwork trying for approving strokes.

My appearance is awful. I dress shoddily as I'm almost 200 lbs. and nothing looks good on my body. I should have three moles removed on my face which are growing and I know they are ugly. My husband always remarks about how ugly they are. I made a pact with myself that if I lose weight I'll have my moles removed—no luck!

Mildred's response provides us with a living example of the TA concept of life positions. She is in the position identified as I'm not OK—You're OK, a position in which one feels inferior to other people. Mildred is struggling against her negative life position, and I get the distinct feeling from her class work that she will in the long run succeed in attaining a better self-image. The main point to be made here is that one's life position has a great deal to do with one's behavior in general, and with one's eating behavior in particular. For example, some people over-eat as a way of temporarily coping with depression. If these same people also suffer from chronic inferiority feelings, they are likely to experience depression and to overeat rather frequently. Clearly, it is of value for overweight persons to develop a greater comprehension of the four basic life positions and their relationship to overeating.

TA attaches great significance to how we perceive ourselves in relation to others. We all have a self-image. We also have images of other people. These images are subjective, and may not correspond with the perceptions and judgments of others. For example, when Mildred's response was read aloud to the TA group, a number of other members protested that Mildred's moles were hardly noticeable, that she was nicely dressed, and so forth. They directly attempted to invalidate her life position. Perhaps they were being kind. Perhaps they really meant what they said. But in any event it was clear that their assurances made little impression on Mildred.

The counseling work of Transactional Analysts suggests that a life position is adopted on the basis of experiences in infancy and early childhood. In *Games People Play* Berne says:

Positions are taken and become fixed surprisingly early, from the second or even the first year to the seventh year of life—in any case long before the individual is competent or experienced enough to make such a serious commitment.*

The life positions arise out of the way children are treated by parents and/or adults acting in parental roles (for example, grandparents, baby-sitters, and preschool teachers). On the

*Eric Berne, *Games People Play* (Paperback: New York: Grove Press, 1967), p. 46.

basis of this early experience children develop attitudes about themselves and others. Some children develop attitudes of trust, autonomy, and competence. Others—the unfortunate ones—develop attitudes of mistrust, guilt, and incompetence, the building blocks of losing life positions.

The four basic life positions identified by TA are:

1. I'm not OK—You're OK
2. I'm OK—You're not OK
3. I'm not OK—You're not OK
4. I'm OK—You're OK

There is only one winning position: I'm OK—You're OK. The other three are losing positions.

TA believes that most children adopt one of the three losing positions, the most common being I'm not OK—You're OK. Relatively few take the winning position, I'm OK—You're OK. These are children who have an exceptionally happy childhood. The child blessed with particularly understanding, sensitive, and nurturing parents will probably decide that he or she is OK and that other people are OK too. But there is another road to the winning position. It is the tough, rocky road of reality. This second road requires that at some time in our adulthood we accept personal responsibility for our feelings and make a *redecision* to adopt the winning position. Toward the end of this chapter you will find a list of practical ways of using the Adult to make such a redecision.

Let us now see how the four life positions relate to the psychology of weight control and the personality structures of overweight persons. After describing each position in general TA terms, I will give a case history of an overweight person in that position and an analysis of his or her Child, Parent, and Adult ego states. Before reading this section you may want to look at Figure 2 for a visual summary of the structure of the personality as described in this book.

I have chosen these case histories because they represent extremes. Such extremes bring out in bold relief some of the

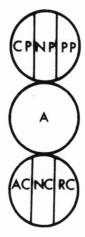

Figure 2. The structure of the personality as conceptualized in this book. *Code:* CP = Controlling Parent, NP = Nurturing Parent, PP = Permissive Parent, A = Adult, AC = Adapted Child, NC = Natural Child, RC = Rebellious Child.

basic psychological principles at work in various overeating patterns.

I'M NOT OK—YOU'RE OK

People in the I'm not OK—You're OK position are the ones who suffer from low self-esteem. The familiar term *inferiority complex,* coined some years ago by the depth psychologist Alfred Adler, was intended for such individuals. The typical person in this life position thinks that he has a serious flaw. He is lacking in creative ability, poise, or maybe he isn't tall enough. However, nobody else in the world has this particular flaw. The rest of the social world is made up of perfect people. He never stops to think that they have flaws as serious as or more serious than his. He is so intent on his own shortcomings that he pays little or no attention to theirs.

Overweight people in the I'm not OK—You're OK position see themselves as flawed by fat. And they do *not* think that fat is beautiful. They associate fat with ugliness. Consequently, they tend to have a very poor body image. At the same time they think that the rest of the people in the world are of normal weight. Their perception of the bodies of other people is distorted by their own sense of discontent. Oh, if they actually think about it from the Adult, they realize that there are plenty of fat people in the world. But most of the time they are perceiving the social world out of the Child, and therefore do not see it as it actually is. These Child perceptions add to their discontent.

An example of how not OK feelings can reside behind unnecessary eating is provided by the behavior of Jack London, famous author of such classics as *The Call of the Wild* and *The Sea Wolf*. It is well known that London was an alcoholic. It is less well known that he ate great quantities when he was depressed. London died a comparatively young man, in his early forties. His death was hastened by the excessive use of alcohol and food. In an authoritative biography by author Richard O'Connor, London's odd food preferences are described. Although he was suffering from uremic poisoning associated with kidney disease, against the advice of his doctors he insisted on gorging himself on raw fish, barbecued pork, underdone mallards, and other undercooked meats. He was, he said, "naturally a meat eater." Apparently London unconsciously associated raw and rare meat with strength, and in failing health it seems likely that his Child magically hoped to draw new life from a Stone Age diet. It also seems likely that London was suffering from a chronic stroke hunger, a deep craving for greater affection in his life. London was born an illegitimate child. He was raised by his natural mother, but not by his natural father. His mother was a rather eccentric person, unable to provide London with much spontaneous attention or affection. In addition, he was poor during childhood and adolescence, and felt humiliated by his poverty. All these experiences contributed to nagging not OK feelings and a constant craving for strokes in the form of praise and recognition in adulthood.

London's life is instructive, and that is why I have briefly related a portion of it. There are certain parallels between this famous man's not OK feelings and the feelings of overeaters in general. My own conviction from working with a great many overweight clients is that the first life position, the I'm not OK —You're OK position, is by far the one most commonly associated with eating problems. At a very general level, I am able to describe the typical personality of such individuals.

Susan E. is presented here as an example of a typical overweight person in the I'm not OK—You're OK life position. Here are the principal characteristics of her personality structure:

1. Susan has a large Controlling Parent. Consequently she is very self-critical, often angry at herself for small errors and petty transgressions. This is a reflection of the way she was treated in early childhood. Her parents were authoritarians, very bossy, and real put-down artists. Her Controlling Parent is forever saying to her Child, "You're too fat," "You should go on a diet," "You shouldn't eat that," and "Don't leave food on your plate." Susan's parents gave her strokes on a conditional basis. There was very little "I love you because you're you." Instead the psychological message was: "I'll love you if . . ." and "You're OK only if . . ." (If you behave nicely, if you are clean, if you tidy up your room, etc.)

2. Susan has a small Nurturing Parent. Susan was not used to receiving unconditional strokes, spontaneous displays of affection, from her parents. As a grownup with a small Nurturing Parent, Susan finds it difficult to stroke herself. She has a hard time saying to herself, "You're doing well," or "That outfit looks nice on you," or "You're a good cook."

3. Susan has a large Adapted Child. She is oversocialized,

conforming too rigidly to the demands of authority figures. She is excessively polite and too concerned with pleasing others. Used to being discounted and belittled as a child, Susan suffers from a chronic stroke hunger. At a deep level of her being she feels unloved and unappreciated. These feelings, rooted in developmental experiences as they are, do not reflect the way her husband, children, and others feel about her. Indeed, her husband is often puzzled when she declares, "I wonder if you really love me." Food for Susan symbolizes love and affection. Feeling inferior, often the victim of vague anxieties, Susan compulsively eats between meals. Her favorite foods are the treat foods of her childhood. Hot chocolate, marshmallows, cookies, candy, and ice cream—these are the foods that give her comfort. But food has no lasting stroke value. Anxiety is only temporarily relieved; not OK feelings are only briefly suppressed. I call the transient stroking effect of food *fake strokes.*

4. Susan has a small Rebellious Child. She has great difficulty expressing aggression, and tends to turn anger in on herself. As a consequence, she is ulcer-prone and has a tendency toward high blood pressure. Her aggression is expressed passively by failing at tasks, by leaving too many things undone, and by nagging her children. Some of her unnecessary eating is out of her Rebellious Child. She cheats on a diet, she gobbles food when her husband is asleep on the recliner in front of the television set, and she sneaks a candy bar when she is on a trip to the supermarket. All these acts are unconscious expressions of anger. But they are weak forms of rebellion. On the whole, she vents her anger in ineffective ways.

5. Susan's small Natural Child is squeezed between her large Adapted Child on one side and her Rebellious Child on the other. As a consequence, she finds it hard just to relax and be herself. Spontaneous expressions of laughter or joy are difficult for her. It has been years since she played with abandon or allowed her feelings a free rein. Similarly, her

eating is not spontaneous. It is planned eating—a diet—out of her Controlling Parent, or compulsive eating out of her Adapted Child, or aggressive eating out of her Rebellious Child. She just doesn't trust herself to eat according to her natural body hunger. She is out of touch with these feelings, feelings arising from her restricted Natural Child.

6. Susan's Adult is heavily contaminated by her Controlling Parent and her Adapted Child. (The term *contamination* is used in TA when either the Parent or the Child encroaches upon the psychological territory of the Adult.) Thus it is difficult for her to think for herself and make responsible decisions. Her Controlling Parent says, "You'd better go on a diet. You're getting too fat!" Her Adapted Child says, "Nobody loves me. Food makes me feel better." Her besieged Adult says weakly, "I don't know what to do." And so she loses a few pounds, only to gain them back.

In traditional clinical psychological terms, Susan is suffering from a chronic neurotic reaction. Neurotic reactions are characterized by high anxiety, internal conflict, and inferiority feelings. One kind of neurotic disorder is the obsessive-compulsive reaction. For example, a person might be obsessed with the idea that everything is dirty, that everything touched fouls the hands with germs. The individual copes with the obsession by compulsively washing his hands many times a day. Similarly, Susan is obsessed with the idea of food. Images of eating her favorite foods intrude upon her thoughts at odd moments of the day. She pushes the unwanted images away, but they quickly return with greater strength. She copes with the obsession by eating several times a day between meals.

As self-defeating as Susan's life position is, there is hope in it. Seeing herself as "not OK fat" means that she is not denying reality. Seeing others as OK means that she is open to help, advice, and information. What she must do is learn effective ways to decontaminate her Adult, reducing the too great influence of her Controlling Parent and her

Adapted Child. She must see her present life position for what it is, and make a conscious decision to work toward the I'm OK—You're OK position. Although difficult, these changes are possible. People do learn, and people do grow. I have seen it happen over and over again. And that, of course, is what this book is all about.

I'M OK—YOU'RE NOT OK

The corpulent character Sir John Falstaff, sidekick of Prince Hal, played principal roles in Shakespeare's plays *Henry IV* and *The Merry Wives of Windsor.* So interesting a character was Falstaff that he inspired the great Italian composer Giuseppe Verdi to write an opera by the same name. To this day the adjective *Falstaffian* is used to suggest a robust fat person who loves to eat huge amounts of food and make merry. But Falstaff was not an admirable character. He was what today we would call a wheeler-dealer, a con artist. He had very little conscience, and was more than willing to take advantage of others for his own selfish gain. These statements well describe the life position designated as I'm OK—You're not OK.

A person in this life position tends to see his relationship to another person in I-it terms, not I-thou terms. This distinction was forcefully pointed out by the theologian Martin Buber. In the I-it relationship, Buber says, the first person sees himself as a real person with needs and feelings but perceives the second person as not truly alive, as a cardboard character in his psychological world. The first person is thus completely egocentric, living only for himself. In contrast, in the I-thou relationship, the first person recognizes that other people have feelings too, and he tries at least some of the time to see things from their point of view.

When egocentric people are overweight they have a hard time comprehending that there is anything wrong with being fat. They may pay lip service to popular values, saying weakly,

"I wish I could lose some weight." But there is no real steam behind the wish. They are just talking. In fact, they resent the importance the culture places on slimness. These are the people who join "fat is beautiful" movements. They conveniently deny that fat is unhealthy, that fat shortens lives.

But fat is ugly because it can be a killer. No reference to the fact that in certain cultures fat women are the ideal can change the deadliness of fat. The I'm OK position regarding fat is an unreal position, a position of utter denial. As a consequence, it is difficult to reach people in this position. They have very little authentic interest in weight control.

Harry Q. is a modern-day Falstaff. He makes his living as a salesman, and is financially successful. He is not above putting over a quick one on his customers, taking advantage of their ignorance whenever possible. He is a great believer in the Roman saying *"Caveat emptor"* or "Buyer beware." Let us present Harry as a typical overweight individual in the I'm OK—You're not OK life position. Here are the principal characteristics of Harry's personality structure:

1. Harry has a large Permissive Parent. Thus he functions with very little conscience, not only in his business dealings, but in his personal relationships. He does not hesitate to manipulate his wife and children to satisfy his own ends. He perceives himself as the lord and master of his household.

    When he overeats, there is no little voice in his head that says, "You should go on a diet," or "Why don't you lose weight?" He has recently developed a habit of stopping in at a coffee shop around 3 P.M. and eating a cheeseburger with fries. He does this with no conscious guilt whatsoever. His weight is approaching three hundred pounds, and the fact causes him very little dismay. Indeed, he unconsciously takes pride in his obesity. It makes him feel important, literally helping him to feel that he is a "big man." As he stuffs himself, the Permissive Parent smiles in benign approval, saying, "Have a second piece of meat, Harry. It looks delicious."

2. Harry has a very small Nurturing Parent. Although Harry's parents were permissive, they were not loving. Basically Harry's parents were emotionally uninvolved with him. They tended to ignore him unless he did something to attract attention. Therefore he received very few unconditional strokes. Spontaneous displays of affection from his mother and father were rare. Instead he received the fake strokes of extra privileges and bribes associated with permissive parental styles. In consequence, Harry, like Susan, suffers from a chronic stroke hunger. For all his posturing and braggadocio, Harry does not enjoy the quiet confidence that he is a loved person. With his shrunken Nurturing Parent, Harry can seldom say to himself such things as: "You really did a good job on that." Although he is consciously in the I'm OK position, this is to a large extent a pose, a sham position, designed to cover up deeply buried not OK feelings.

3. The big bad boy in Harry's personality structure is his Rebellious Child. In the ordinary person, the Rebellious Child is the source of impulsive decisions and aggressive behavior. In Harry's case, these traits are greatly exaggerated. An apt synonym for Harry's Rebellious Child would be the Spoiled Brat. An actual spoiled brat wants his way without regard for the feelings of others. Harry's Rebellious Child or Spoiled Brat is no different. He rides roughshod over the psychological needs of his wife and children. On Sunday the family goes where Harry wants to go. There is no discussion. The family eats what Harry wants to eat. Their preferences are not considered. At the dinner table, he serves himself first. He takes the choicest cuts of meat and the tastiest morsels of food. He often treats himself to two thick T-bone steaks for dinner. (You're wondering about the expense. There's no money problem. Harry is financially successful.) He frequently drinks three

or four glasses of beer with his meals. I have already mentioned his habit of having a cheeseburger in a coffee shop in the afternoon. He also usually raids the refrigerator about midnight, feasting on arrays of cold cuts and other delicatessen items. Two more cans of beer top off the feast. When he is eating lunch out with business associates, he favors a particular buffet restaurant where he can go back for second slices of roast beef and load up his plate with extra pieces of fried chicken.

Although Harry likes almost all foods, he has a particular fondness for meats, particularly beef. This ties in with his big Rebellious Child. At the psychological level, eating meat symbolizes an act of aggression for Harry. Cutting with a knife, ripping meat with his teeth from a chicken leg, chewing up something that resists, are all ways in which Harry's hostile aggressive impulses toward others are channeled into a socially safe behavior pattern. The eating of meat unconsciously gives Harry a sense of greater mastery and control over life.

4. Harry has a small Adapted Child. His Child never had to learn to mold itself to the demands of controlling parents. In consequence, although Harry manages to bump along in the world without getting into actual trouble with the law, he is at his core a lawbreaker. Thus he cheats others and practices various forms of deception whenever he can. Susan was described as oversocialized, too responsible for her own good. (Remember, she had a large Adapted Child.) Conversely, Harry might be described as undersocialized. He superficially conforms to society's rules only because it suits his long-range interests. Although Harry has a small Adapted Child, we have already noted that he does suffer from stroke hunger. This accounts for some of his unnecessary eating. Feeling unloved, he uses food as an unsatisfactory substitute for affection.

5. Harry has a small Natural Child. It occupies a shrunken psychological territory between his Rebellious Child and

his Adapted Child. Although superficially Harry gives the impression of a person with a big Natural Child, it is all a pose. He tells jokes and clowns around a lot at parties, but it is all for effect. He has very little capacity for spontaneous play, almost never relaxing and having a good time without regard for the effect his behavior is having on others. When he plays poker with his cronies, he sees the game as a power struggle. He does not enjoy the process of the game, but is preoccupied with the end result of the evening in terms of wins and losses. This explains why he is an impatient card player, often saying, "Deal! Deal!" or "C'mon, let's get it moving!"

With a small Natural Child, Harry does very little eating out of a state of physical hunger. He does not ask himself, "Am I hungry?" Instead the question is, "Is it time to eat?" He does not ask himself, "Am I full?" His concern is, "Is there enough food on the table for me to have seconds and thirds?" Almost completely unaware of his momentary state of physiological hunger, he doesn't know when it has been satisfied. When he ceases to eat it is not from an internal cue such as a feeling of fullness. The cue that tells him to stop is external: The food has run out or it's time to do something else. Consequently Harry eats past feeling satisfied. He eats until he is bloated and in a semistupor.

6. Harry's Adult is contaminated primarily by his Permissive Parent and his Rebellious Child. When it comes to decisions about eating, he does very little real thinking for himself. His Permissive Parent gives him the license to devour great quantities of food. And his Rebellious Child supplies the wish to do so. These joint influences on his Adult have the effect of removing his eating behavior from the rational domain.

There isn't a great deal of hope for weight loss in Harry's I'm OK—You're not OK position. He has little motivation to change. In order for behavioral change to take place, a person like Harry has to suffer more. Something has to draw him up short. A heart attack, a stroke, a diagnosis of diabetes, his wife having an affair, or some other loss might wake him up to the long-range no-win life position he is in. However, until something negative really happens, he moves through life in his fool's paradise. The Harrys of the world are generally poor candidates for counseling or psychotherapy. But if they do give up their I'm OK—You're not OK position, they tend to make rapid psychological progress. This is because they are often intelligent, and possess Adult ego states that can learn fast under the right conditions.

In traditional clinical psychological terms, Harry is suffering from an antisocial reaction, which is classified as a personality disorder. Antisocial individuals, also called sociopaths, have no concern for others and feel no guilt or anxiety. They tend to be bossy, glib, manipulative, and impulsive. Although they make others suffer a great deal, they suffer very little within themselves, sleeping well at night and digesting their food well.

I'M NOT OK—YOU'RE NOT OK

The I'm not OK—You're not OK life position is the most unfortunate of the life positions discussed thus far. It represents a very negative view of life. Not only does the person in this life position suffer from severe inferiority feelings, he also finds himself unable to trust others. Thus even if he is miserable, he will not seek the services of physicians, psychiatrists, psychologists, nutritionists, counselors, social workers, or other professionals who might be able to help him. He is trapped in a psychological web of his own making. The person in the I'm not OK—You're not OK life position tends to spend his days in a state of permanent depression. He seldom smiles, has few friends, and does his work with a cloud of gloom hanging over his head. A word sometimes used to describe such persons is *alienated,* meaning they find it difficult to feel that they really belong anywhere. They are the world's outsiders.

Clarence C. is a typical individual in the I'm Not OK—You're not OK life position. He has been employed as a research librarian for more than fifteen years. A bachelor, he leads a molelike existence, shuttling between the library's shelves of research documents and the loneliness of his small apartment. Although he is about seventy pounds overweight, he discusses his weight problem with no one. Here are the principal characteristics of Clarence's personality structure:

1. Clarence's social behavior is contaminated by a very large Controlling Parent. His actual parents were strident, demanding, often unreasonable people who lectured Clarence sternly about what is right and wrong in this world and what makes for good and bad people. Unfortunately, they often disagreed between themselves about questions of propriety, and left poor Clarence with a Controlling Parent that is severe and at the same time confused. Clarence tries hard to function in the social world, but he finds that the price he must pay for conforming to his Controlling Parent is a great deal of bottled-up rage.

2. As you might expect, Clarence has a very small Nurturing Parent. When Clarence was a child his parents did not give him unconditional strokes. Displays of affection had to be earned, and even then his parents gave such displays briefly and grudgingly. Their inability to meet his early emotional needs contributed greatly to Clarence's lack of trust in others. He does not expect other people to really care about him. He feels that others will fail him, just as his parents failed him when he was a child.

3. The primary psychological culprit in Harry's eating problem is his Rebellious Child. He has a very large Rebellious Child arising out of deep frustrations associated with the demands of his confused Controlling Parent. As his general rage at life surfaces, he expresses his resentment in a fairly "safe" way: by consuming large quantities of food. When

the sun goes down, Clarence, like a latter-day wolfman, turns into an eating animal. In the loneliness of his apartment, with the curtains drawn, he sometimes binges uncontrollably for hours. The animal comparison is not too far-fetched. He often eats only with his hands, making small grunting noises as he gobbles. His cheeks bulge, and his mouth is so full that he can hardly chew. Still he stuffs food in on top of food. When Clarence is in one of these states he is like a person in a trance. He barely knows what he is doing. When he "comes to" he surveys the gnawed bones, the bits of food on the floor, and his greasy hands with mixed feelings of disgust (coming from his Controlling Parent) and satisfaction (coming from his Rebellious Child).

No one sees Clarence's secret eating. He takes a small sack lunch to work, eats it alone at his desk. If he stops in at a coffee shop, he orders moderate amounts. On the social level, Clarence is a conformist. It is when he is away from the potentially judging eyes of others that his Rebellious Child takes over and runs his behavior. The solitary gorging symbolizes for Clarence, "I don't have to do what they tell me to do." His Controlling Parent says that he should eat politely with utensils, and Clarence rebels by eating with his hands. His Controlling Parent says that he should eat in moderation, and Clarence rebels by stuffing himself.

4. Clarence has a relatively small Adapted Child. He is really only half socialized, and conforms outwardly not out of acceptance of social norms, but out of fear of the punitive wrath of his Controlling Parent. When he transgresses, it will say to him, "You're stupid," or "You're worthless," or "You're a fool." There were very few loving strokes in Clarence's childhood, and there are even fewer strokes in his adult life. Thus Clarence's Adapted Child blindly stuffs him with food in a futile effort to stuff up the emptiness of his existence.

5. Clarence has an almost nonexistent Natural Child. He gets no fun out of life, his speech is stilted and mechanical, and he forces a smile when something funny is said. In brief, he

is almost completely lacking in spontaneity of expression or behavior. He does not start and stop eating out of organic hunger. His voracious appetite is determined by his Rebellious Child's need to express anger and his Adapted Child's craving for affection. Thus he cannot trust his Natural Child as a guide to eating behavior. His Natural Child does not occupy a sufficiently large region of the Child's total domain to be of any consequence.

6. Clarence's Adult is very heavily contaminated by his mixed-up Controlling Parent and his angry Rebellious Child. Like an erratic robot, his behavior is directed by conflicting programs. His fellow workers, noting his eccentricities and mechanical ways, call him Crazy Clarence behind his back. With a half-functioning Adult, Clarence is unable to discover for himself a sound and sensible way of eating. Occasionally he goes on crash diets or fasts—behaviors determined by his Controlling Parent. However, most of the time he indulges himself in the evening binges already described.

In traditional clinical psychological terms, Clarence is suffering from a borderline psychotic reaction. Psychotic reactions are characterized by bizarre thoughts, personality disorganization, a lack of trust in others, and related symptoms. As already noted, he is alienated and angry. He is "mad" in the psychiatric sense. (It is perhaps more than a coincidence that the word "mad" is used as a synonym for anger and also as a colloquialism for psychotic reactions.) The clinical term for a condition in which a person has fits of uncontrolled eating is *bulimia*. And bulimia is, of course, a kind of transient madness. It is not the Adult that says to eat to the point of near unconsciousness. Only a crazy Child would direct one to do such a thing.

There is much less hope in Clarence's I'm not OK— You're not OK position than in the two life positions previously discussed. How do you reach a person like Clarence? He won't seek help voluntarily—remember, he has almost no capacity to trust. The Clarences of the world usually are not helped. They remain alienated, depressed, angry, and obese. Sometimes they even lose their tenuous hold on reality and manifest the symptoms of a blatant psychosis. If they hallucinate, become delusional, threaten people, injure themselves, or inflict bodily injury on others, they will be hospitalized as mental patients. Under such circumstances, they are brought to the attention of psychotherapists and other members of the healing professions. If the therapist is sensitive, if the hospital provides a nurturing environment, if a Clarence hurts enough to take a chance on trusting another person, it sometimes happens that such an individual changes, grows, and finds out that at the deepest level of his being he is OK after all. These are all big *ifs*. Nonetheless, not even the near-mad life position is devoid of hope. Positive changes can take place even when a person is behind the worst kind of psychological eightball. I have seen it happen more than once.

I'M OK—YOU'RE OK

The I'm OK—You're OK life position is the "up" position. A person in this position feels that life is worth living, that he is in charge of his own fate, that he makes things happen. He feels that he is OK to the core of his being. He may be self-critical, but he will not put himself down from his Critical Parent. He may say to himself from his Adult, "You ate too much because you ate too fast. Next time try slowing down, chewing more completely—not putting one bite in on top of another one." But he will *not* say to himself, "You slob. You're nothing but a hog! You overate again. You're nothing but a hopeless compulsive eater." Such self-criticisms only make a person depressed, and drive him deeper into an I'm not OK position.

As noted previously, there are two ways to arrive at the I'm OK—You're OK life position. One is the easy road, the road of a happy childhood with sensitive and understanding parents. Children who receive many unconditional strokes, who are allowed freedom in growing up, but not license, who are allowed to participate in family decisions, and who have parents with rational eating habits will probably be a normal weight and will know that they are OK and that others are OK. Unfortunately, not everyone is so lucky. If you are one of those upon whom the Fates have smiled, you are probably not reading this book.

We thus turn to the hard road, the road of personal responsibility and conscious decisions. This is the second road by which the I'm OK—You're OK life position is reached. Although it is a hard road, it is one well worth traveling. When you arrive at the positive position as a result of your own efforts, you place a great value on it, and you are not likely to give up lightly. It was purchased at too high a price. I am therefore convinced that some of the healthiest people in the world are those who started out in early childhood from one of the negative positions. Their adult strength of character was forged out of the fire of adversity.

Perhaps you are familiar with the famous poem "Invictus" (Latin for "Unconquered") by William Ernest Henley. It says very much the same thing in metaphorical form that I have said in the above paragraph. Henley lost a leg in early childhood and nearly lost another as an adult. *Invictus* reveals the brave I'm OK stance he took against the adversities of life. It shows how the I'm OK position can be the result of a conscious decision. i have often recommended that persons struggling toward a positive life position memorize it and recite it mentally at appropriate times. Here is the poem:

> Out of the night that covers me,
>   Black as the Pit from pole to pole,
> I thank whatever gods may be
>   For my unconquerable soul.
>
> In the fell clutch of circumstance
>   I have not winced nor cried aloud.
> Under the bludgeonings of chance
>   My head is bloody, but unbowed.

Beyond this place of wrath and tears
  Looms but the horror of the shade,
And yet the menace of the years
  Finds, and shall find me, unafraid.

It matters not how strait the gate,
  How charged with punishments the scroll,
I am the master of my fate:
  I am the captain of my soul.

One of the frequent objections tendered against the I'm OK —You're OK life position is: "Maybe I'm OK, but I'm not so sure about other people! Does adopting this position mean that I've got to like and trust everybody?" Of course not. The fourth position is not a fool's position. The person in the fourth position approaches other people expecting to like them, hoping for the best. But if a particular person turns out to be untrustworthy, the individual with a healthy personality will not use this as evidence that everyone is no good. He will simply guard himself in his dealings with the individual he can't trust.

Eve G. is a person in the I'm OK—You're OK position. She is a nurse, married, and the mother of two children. She reached the positive position by the hard road. Of her own volition she has sought psychotherapy, gone to weight-control groups, taken my psychology of weight-control class, and studied psychology and TA. Over a two-year period she lost more than sixty pounds, and has maintained a normal weight for more than a year.

When I first met her, her self-concept was: "I'm fat and ugly. I must not be very bright. I have no self-discipline. I can't understand why my husband says he loves me. I'm always tired. I'm a terrible nurse, and I'm afraid I'm going to hurt someone someday with all the mistakes I make." Now, three years later, she has a completely different self-concept. I know that she sees herself as a beautiful and intelligent person—and she is—although she doesn't say so directly. She *does* say, "I've learned a lot. I know I'm OK now. Although I've got a lot more to learn,

I'm on the right road at last!" Here are the characteristics of Eve's present personality structure:

1. Eve has succeeded in reducing the size of her once large Controlling Parent. She has learned that her old habit of putting herself down was the result of replaying old Parent tapes. Now she turns off the Controlling Parent when it starts telling her she is not OK, when it begins to lecture her for her failings, and when it becomes excessively punitive. She no longer thinks in terms of: "You're looking simply awful. What's wrong with you? You'd better get yourself on a diet!" Instead she thinks from her Adult: "I've gained two pounds. I'm going to cut out and cut down on food where I realistically can."

2. Eve has expanded the influence of her Nurturing Parent. She has learned how to stroke herself, how to tell herself she's OK. Inside herself, she does not adopt a pose of false modesty for her accomplishments. When she does something particularly well in her nursing job, she says to herself, "That was an excellent job! You found the patient's vein for the glucose solution on one try. Great!" In the past, her Critical Parent would have found fault with her when she made an error, but her Nurturing Parent was usually silent when she did something right. Now when she leaves a little food on her plate or passes up a dessert, her Nurturing Parent says, "That was good. You're succeeding. You're doing fine."

3. Eve's Adapted Child is much smaller than it once was. In the past she suffered from a chronic stroke hunger, and tried to fill her need for affection with food. Now she strokes herself more adequately from her Nurturing Parent. Also, she has learned how to get more and better strokes from others, particularly her husband. Thus she feels much more significant as a person. Her need for symbolic strokes in the form of food has given way to a capacity to give and receive real strokes—which are, of course, more satisfying.

Eve's Rebellious Child exerts a minimum of influence. She seldom feels the need to express aggression in childish ways—by screaming at her husband, by breaking something, by being late for work, by making mistakes on the job, by sneaking food when her husband is not looking, by going on angry binges. She has found effective ways to assert herself out of her Adult, and thus she no longer suffers from a pool of bottled-up anger. She is much more relaxed, calm, and free of nervous tension with a smaller Rebellious Child.

5. Eve's Natural Child now occupies the majority of the psychological domain of her Child. She has learned how to play, how to have fun, how to let go and enjoy life. She laughs when a joke is funny to her, but she does not give an artificial social laugh when she sees nothing to laugh about. She is taking tennis lessons. And she is finding that the important thing for her is not winning, but the sheer fun of being on a court and knocking a ball around. The *process* of the game is much more important than the *goal* of winning the game. She is applying that insight to all areas of her life. She is seeing for the first time that the process of living, the experiences we have along the pathway of life, are more important than the goals toward which we sometimes compulsively struggle. In touch with her Natural Child, Eve lives in the *now*, not in some abstract future that may never come.

Being in touch with her Natural Child also means that she has begun more and more to eat in terms of real organic hunger. When she is eating, her Adult inquires of her Natural Child, "Are you full now? Do you want to stop? Would you feel cheated if you passed up the dessert?" In touch with her Natural Child, she is able to answer these questions honestly. In the past, she did not know if she was actually hungry or not. She ate because she was craving affection, because she was angry, or because of external stimuli that induced her to eat. Now that she has tuned into her Natural Child, these other goads to behavior have diminished in importance.

6. Eve has almost completely decontaminated her Adult. The Parent and the Child no longer encroach upon the territory of the Adult. When she begins to indulge in self-criticism, or when she feels strong emotion rising, she asks herself, "Where is this really coming from? Do *I* actually feel this way? Or am I just letting something push my Parent button or my Child button? How do I really want to act now? What do I really think now? What do I really feel now?" She has learned to place a thinking delay between a situation and the response to that situation. When she eats, she is aware of what she is eating, why she is eating, and how the food tastes. By placing the Adult in charge of her eating behavior, her Natural Child can relax and enjoy food without guilt.

DECIDING TO BE OK

It is my experience that the vast majority of overweight people are in the first position described, the I'm not OK—You're OK position. They feel unhappy with their fat, and they feel that there is hope somewhere, but they search in the wrong places. They think that this new diet, or that new shot, or acupuncture, or something else will be the magic key that will open the door to the kingdom of normal weight. But you see now that these are all superficial appeals to the Child. There *is* hope, of course. Persons in the I'm not OK—You're OK position are right about that. The hope resides in learning new approaches to eating, gathering information, and placing the Adult in charge of one's eating behavior.

A relatively small percentage of overweight people are in the second (I'm OK—You're not OK) and third (I'm not OK—You're not OK) life positions. These individuals are harder to reach than persons in the first position. They seldom read books like this one. Persons in the I'm OK—You're not OK position are not looking for answers. They are content with themselves

—at least at a conscious level. Persons in the I'm not OK— You're not OK position might look for answers if they trusted anyone else enough to do so. But because they consider others not OK, they don't think others can help. Thus they avoid physicians, weight-control groups, and sources of information such as books.

If you are reading this book with a good deal of spontaneous interest, the odds are high that your life position is either the first one described (I'm not OK—You're OK) or the last (I'm OK —You're OK). It is my observation that people who have recently arrived at the fourth position by their own efforts seek to entrench the position by continued reading and information-seeking.

If you are in a negative life position, don't waste your time playing the blaming game. You may feel like saying, "If only my parents hadn't been such authoritarians, I'd be OK now." But keep in mind that your parents very probably had good intentions. Most parents do. Adopting a negative life position is a decision made by the Child ego state, and your Child may not have recorded or interpreted your parents correctly. Perhaps you have heard this saying: "I know you believe you understand what I said. But I'm not sure you realize that what you heard is not what I meant!" That is the defense that can be offered in favor of your parents. Your Child may have distorted their meanings.

In any event, a negative life position was a decision made by the Child. You're a grownup now, and what was decided years ago can be *redecided*. Redeciding a life position requires that you *think* (use your Adult) and *contact your feelings* (know your Child). A conscious redecision made by your Adult can move you out of one of the negative life positions decided upon by your Child years ago. And what is the conscious redecision? Just this: "I'm going to be an OK person. And other people are OK too."

In order to make a conscious redecision that will stick, it is helpful to remember a set of positive affirmations. Here are the affirmations:

1. I'm OK. I'm OK just because I'm me. At my core, my inner being has value—unconditional value.
2. I will not waste time blaming my parents for my life position. My present life position is my responsibility. What happened in the past is water under the bridge.
3. I will not allow myself the indulgence of self-criticism. It is useless to put myself down and call myself names. It only makes me depressed.
4. I will stroke myself. I will tell myself I'm OK. I will praise myself within myself when I do well.
5. I will recognize that much of my excessive eating is a search for strokes, a substitute for real affection. I will learn more effective ways to obtain strokes.
6. I will recognize that some of my excessive eating may be a way of expressing anger, a way of dealing with my aggressive tendencies. I will learn more constructive ways to assert myself.
7. I will make greater efforts to get in touch with my Natural Child, to relax, and to just be myself. I want to find out what it is to eat spontaneously some of the time—to start eating because I'm really hungry and to stop eating because I'm really full.
8. I am going to have my Adult take the prime responsibility for my eating behavior and my weight. I can learn to become an increasingly rational person, facing reality and accepting responsibility for my behavior. My Adult will allow my Natural Child to play in appropriate circumstances, but my Adult will remain in charge.
9. Other people are OK. On the whole, I like people and expect well of them.

Some of my clients have memorized this list of positive life position affirmations. They mentally recite the affirmations from time to time, and in various circumstances, as a way of consolidating their redecision to become OK persons.

6

Fat-Making Transactions

How would you answer this question: *Who* is making you fat? Ask a group of overweight persons this question and you will often hear such answers as: "My husband!" or "My wife!" or "My mother!" or "My father!" or "My children!" or "My best friend!" Of course, the question is a loaded one. It implies that you are free to shift the blame for eating indiscretions onto others. Now, it is true that your behavior is a response to the behavior of others. But this is only a half-truth. The whole truth is that their behavior is a response to your behavior and your behavior is a response to their behavior and their behavior is a response to your behavior and your behavior is a response to their behavior, and so on. Asking *who* is at fault is like trying to solve the proverbial chicken and the egg problem. Cause and effect are so intertwined in human relations that the search for culprits and villains is often futile.

The above line of thinking brings us to something called the *interpersonal theory of psychopathology.* One of the deans of American psychiatry, Harry Stack Sullivan, is credited with developing this point of view. In brief, the idea is that when a person suffers from a psychological-emotional disturbance, what is "sick" is not the sufferer, not the tyrant in his environment who is "driving him crazy," but *the relationship.* It is the husband-wife, parent-child, or friend-friend relationship that needs "curing," not the individuals involved. The notion is that the relationship is a Gestalt, an organized whole in which the total pattern is more than the sum of its parts. Each person plays a part in creating the relationship's pattern, each person contributes a piece to the puzzle. This approach to psychological suffering avoids the oversimplified "solution" of blaming one person and absolving another. In other words, "It takes two to tango."

Although it takes two to tango, it takes only one to break off the dance. If you are playing a game of chess and your opponent suddenly stands up and says, "I don't want to play anymore," the game ends! Similarly, in human relations, pathological patterns can be disrupted if one person decides to stop playing the game. In Chapter Seven, we will discuss games fat people play. In this chapter, I will introduce the concept of *transactions,* fundamental patterns that underlie the more complex patterns called games.

A transaction requires at least two people interacting with each other. It contains two elements, a stimulus and a response. If someone sees you in the hallway at work and says hello, that is a *transactional stimulus.* If you smile and say hello back, that is a *transactional response.* The two of you have just completed a transaction. And what is the point of such a transaction? Why do we engage in the endless "Hellos" of our lives at places of employment, in supermarkets, at church picnics, at family get-togethers, and so forth? In the language of TA, we are "stroking" each other. According to TA, the prime motive for human interaction is the need for *strokes.* If this sounds far-fetched to you, consider what it would be like to have a job where no one said hello to you, where you received no recognition at all, where you were an invisible person. It would be terrible. Solitary confinement, one of the worst of human punishments, puts the prisoner into an environment totally devoid of strokes.

Actually, *any* form of human attention, even a put-down, has a certain amount of stroke value. In TA, strokes that reduce your sense of value—that say "You're not OK"—are called *dis-*

counts. Discounts are thus negative strokes, and they are painful, but they are better than no strokes at all. At least they tell you that you exist. Many children and adults have gotten so used to discounts that they actively seek them, and this tendency plays an important role in fat-making transactions. Let us be alert to this fact as we explore the various kinds of transactions in the next few pages.

The important role that transactions play in excessive eating can hardly be overestimated. Think of all the situations in which we eat in the presence of others: family meals, holiday celebrations, picnics, weddings, dinner parties, lunch with a co-worker, parent and child having a meal at an amusement park. It is obvious that we often eat in the presence of others. What is not so obvious is that the things they say to us, and the things we say to them, have a profound influence on our eating behavior. And it is not only the things we explicitly say with words that affect the way we eat; it is also the things we implicitly "say" with facial expressions, gestures, and body positions. In various ways our verbal and nonverbal transactions may either induce us to eat or inhibit us from eating.

TA specifies three basic kinds of transactions. These are: (1) complementary transactions, (2) crossed transactions, and (3) ulterior transactions. Let us see how each of these kinds of transactions can in its own way be fat-making.

COMPLEMENTARY TRANSACTIONS

In *Games People Play* Berne describes a complementary transaction as one in which the response to a transactional stimulus is appropriate and expected. When such a transaction is illustrated on a TA diagram, the lines running to and from ego states are parallel. Figure 3 illustrates an Adult-Adult complementary transaction, one of several kinds of parallel transactions.

People engage in complementary transactions for a variety of

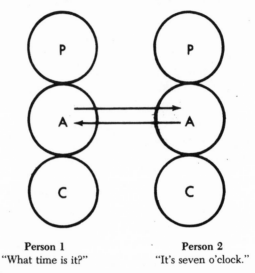

Person 1   Person 2
"What time is it?"   "It's seven o'clock."

Figure 3. An example of a complementary transaction.

reasons: to receive a positive stroke, to give a positive stroke, to receive a discount (or a negative stroke), to give a discount, to consolidate the life position, or to avoid a hassle at the moment. Communication consisting of a series of complementary reactions can go on indefinitely. In this section I will identify four kinds of fat-making complementary transactions: (1) Parent-Parent transactions, (2) Child-Child transactions, (3) Parent-Child transactions, and (4) Child-Parent transactions.

Parent-Parent Transactions

A Parent-Parent transaction is one in which the Parent of person 1 makes a judgmental statement to the Parent of person 2. The Parent of person 2 basically agrees with the statement, perhaps adds to it in some way, and feeds the same biased notion back to person 1.

A husband and a wife are finishing dinner. There is still quite a bit of food on the table, and they are looking for excuses to polish it off. They may swap prejudices from their Parent ego states as a way of giving themselves permission to overeat:

HUSBAND: We always end up throwing away food. Let's finish up what's left. [He is parroting something his mother used to say.]

WIFE: Yes, we should. I was taught "Waste not, want not."

Sometimes a third party is the target of a fat-making Parent-Parent transaction. In the following case, the fat is made on the third party, not the two parties to the transaction. Susan's parents are talking about her within her range of hearing:

MOTHER: Susan is getting so fat. I think she takes after her Aunt Jane.

FATHER: Yeah, I see what you mean. She's getting a big rear end just like Jane. Too bad. It must be genetic.

This kind of careless conversation on the part of Susan's parents may adversely affect her self-concept.

Child-Child Transactions

A Child-Child transaction is one in which the Child of person 1 sends a message with an emotional content (i.e., depression, anger, happiness, joy, pain) to the Child of person 2. The Child of person 2 is at the moment on the same emotional wavelength, and sends a similar message back to the Child of person 1.

Marsha and Alice are having lunch together at a coffee shop. They are both supposedly "on a diet," and they have had broiled beef patties with cottage cheese. As they are sipping their black coffee after the plates are cleared away, Marsha picks up the attractive menu and begins looking at the desserts. Suddenly a gleam enters her eyes. A devilish smile appears on her face. She is entering her Child, and her behavior is inducing Alice to enter her own Child.

MARSHA: What do you think? Should we cheat just once and order a sundae?

ALICE: Let's! I haven't had a sundae in weeks!

Ann is taking her five-year-old granddaughter Sally to an amusement park. Suddenly Ann spots the cotton candy machine. Her eyes begin to glow, memories of her childhood flow back into her mind, and she exclaims, "Oh, Sally, look! Cotton candy! Would you like some?"

Sally responds enthusiastically, "Yes, Grandma!"

Ann and Sally—though years apart—have just engaged in a Child-Child transaction.

Child-Child transactions are likely to take place under any set of circumstances that encourages regression to a more infantile level of behavior: visiting an amusement park, going to a party, eating out, or having a few too many drinks. In various ways all these situations may put a damper of the Adult's capacity to function.

Parent-Child Transactions

In complementary Parent-Child transactions the Parent of person 1 "speaks down" to the Child of person 2, and the Child of person 2 "looks up" to and agrees with the Parent of person 1. The person speaking from the Parent is in the one-up position, and the person responding from the Child is in the one-down position. When people get "high and mighty" with you, when they try to manipulate you by judging or evaluating you, they are usually aiming their messages from their Parent ego state to your Child.

A typical example of a Parent-Child transaction is being a dinner guest. By definition, a guest is on someone else's territory. This automatically places the host or hostess in the one-up position and the guest in the one-down position. Let us say that dessert arrives, and the hostess tries to get the guest to eat it. Perhaps the guest is full or is trying to lose weight. However, the hostess says, "I made it just for you. You've got to eat some."

If the guest gives in and weakly responds, "OK, I'll have some," a Parent-Child transaction has taken place.

When children are growing up, many Parent-Child transactions of the fat-making variety may take place. Here are some familiar examples:

MOTHER: You've got to finish everything on your plate or you can't leave the table!

CHILD: OK, Mommy! [The child is this example already has a big Adapted Child, a mommy-pleaser.]

MOTHER: (In a bossy voice) You just have to eat all of your vegetables!

CHILD: OK, OK. I'll do it.

Many such Parent-Child transactions in childhood condition us to accept passively the dictates of parental figures. Too often we feel even as adults that we must obey when someone else tells us to eat.

Child-Parent Transactions

Complementary Child-Parent transactions require that the Child of person 1 look to the Parent of person 2 for advice, an evaluation, or permission. They also require that the Parent of person 2 respond to the Child of person 1.

Let us say that a wife, Emily, has put her husband, Carl, on a diet. Contradicting her own good intentions, she has baked Carl's favorite cake. After dinner, she is cutting cake for herself and the children as Carl looks on.

CARL: (Almost whining) Can I have a piece of cake too?
EMILY: (Thinking it over, and deciding to be a nice mommy)
Certainly, sweetheart. We'll make an exception.

Again, we are conditioned from childhood to ask for permission and advice. Persons with strong Adult ego states very seldom ask for permission or advice about eating. They do not cast others in parental roles by asking questions from their Child.

CROSSED TRANSACTIONS

In a crossed transaction the response to a transactional stimulus is inappropriate and unexpected, and communication is broken off. When a crossed transaction is illustrated on a TA diagram, the lines running to and from ego states cross each other. Figure 4 illustrates a crossed transaction. In my experience, the most common kind of fat-making crossed transaction is Parent-Child, Parent-Child. In this transaction, the Parent of person 1 addresses the Child of person 2. Person 2 resents being spoken to at the lower level and flips up to his own Parent ego state. Person 2 thus addresses the Child of person 1. The transaction reminds one of crossed swords, pointing downward. When people bicker, they engage in crossed transactions.

Below are a few examples of this kind of crossed transaction. Keep in mind that it is not always possible to tell from words whether a message is coming from the Parent or the Adult. Body language and facial expressions which suggest that one person is judging or evaluating another are indicators that the Parent has been activated.

HUSBAND: You're getting much too fat! Go on a diet!
WIFE: And you! Do you think you're Prince Charming? Look at your gut!

MOTHER: Now look here, young lady, you're not going to have any more desserts until you lose ten pounds!

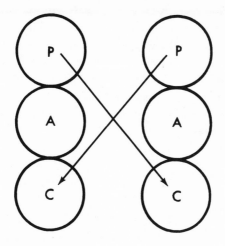

Husband
"You're getting much too fat! Go on a diet!"

Wife
"And you! Do you think you're Prince Charming? Look at your gut!"

Figure 4. An example of a crossed transaction.

TEEN-AGER: I can eat if I want to. You can't stop me. Don't try to tell me what to do!

MOTHER: You can't have any more candy today! [She and her young child are in a supermarket. The child has taken candy off a rack. The mother forcibly takes the candy out of the child's hand.]

CHILD: You're the meanest mother in the world! [This is from the child's Parent, being a judgment leveled against the mother.]

Crossed transactions of the kind described above result in bad feelings. They are an exchange of discounts, resulting in the collection of brown stamps. The brown stamps, which are collected hurts or anger, are subsequently traded in for food, angry binges, and the like. A common racket indulged in by over-weight persons is to set up a crossed transaction so that they can receive discounts and collect some brown stamps! Yes, people in the "not OK" position often initiate transactions designed to prove to themselves that they are in fact not OK. When this is confirmed by the responses of another, the first individual is driven deeper into his negative life position, and he feels increasingly justified in overeating.

ULTERIOR TRANSACTIONS

In ulterior transactions more than two ego states are active at the same time. Thus ulterior transactions are more complex than complementary or crossed transactions. The key to understanding ulterior transactions is to appreciate the fact that persons may be sending and receiving one set of messages at a social level and simultaneously sending and receiving a different set of messages at a psychological level. The *social level* is the level of the message that is apparent or held forth to view. The *psychological level* is ulterior or hidden from view.

Let's say that a particular mother is too thin. She is convinced that she is in constant danger of becoming obese. At a shopping center, she and her slightly overweight twelve-year-old daughter walk by an ice cream parlor. When the daughter asks for a treat the mother protests at first, but ends up buying the treat for her daughter. The mother sips black coffee and smokes a cigarette while her daughter consumes a triple-scoop sundae with three kinds of sauces. While they are seated, there is the following exchange:

MOTHER: (Sternly) Now listen, Susan. Tomorrow I want you to go back on your diet.
DAUGHTER: (Placatingly) OK, Mom. Starting tomorrow I'll really try to stick to my diet.

The transaction is Parent-Child at the social level. But what is happening at the psychological level? This particular mother gets a great deal of secondhand satisfaction from watching her daughter eat. Her Child is saying, "Eat for me. You see how I have to suffer to keep my figure. I can't eat, can't enjoy myself." Her daughter's Child is responding, "OK, Mom. I want you to be happy. I'll do some of your eating for you." Figure 5 illustrates the ulterior transaction that has taken place.

Mothers like the one in this example often wonder why when they "have such good eating habits" they have overweight children. They fail to see the tremendously important part that psychological messages play in fostering overeating behavior.

Close to the opening of this chapter, the Parent-Parent trans-

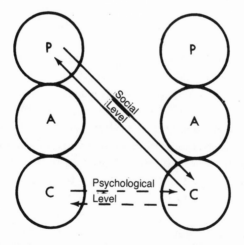

Mother	Daughter
"Tomorrow I want you to go back on your diet."	"OK, Mom. Starting tomorrow I'll really try to stick to my diet."
("Eat for me.")	("OK, Mom. I want you to be happy. I'll do some of your eating for you.")

Figure 5. An example of an ulterior transaction.

action of a particular married couple was offered as one kind of fat-making complementary transaction. The husband said, "We always end up throwing away food. Let's finish up what's left." The wife replied, "Yes, we should. I was taught 'Waste not, want not.'" Let us now assume that there are two more messages being swapped at the psychological level. His Child may be saying to her Child, "I can't leave fried chicken alone." And her Child may be replying to his Child, "Neither can I!" Thus what superficially looks like a rather simple transaction may be quite complex if the psychological level is included. Most fat-making transactions contain ulterior aspects such as these, and it is this hidden level that plays an important part in fat-making games and scripts.

A wife, Frances, says to her husband, "Dan, I've been reading about the dangers of overweight. Do you think you ought to lose a few pounds?" Dan answers, "I'm glad you brought it up. I just read an interesting article about a new high-protein diet that I'm going to try." At the social level, this is an Adult-Adult transaction in which some information is swapped. However, while Frances is speaking, she is passing to her husband his second helping of baked beans. Her Child is communicating, "Here, honey. I baked these beans just for you. All my love for you is in them." His Child is responding, "Thanks, sweetheart. I just can't resist baked beans when you fix them your special way." The transaction is ulterior. They are kidding each other. The words are a smoke screen covering their real feelings.

Rose and Marge, friends, are eating together at a luncheonette. They are both eying the display of pies in a nearby cabinet. Rose says, "Do you realize that a piece of pie can have as much as four hundred calories?" Marge responds, "And it is loaded with sugar and hydrogenated fat." At the social level, the transaction is Adult-Adult. However, Rose says at the psychological level, "But I don't care. I'm going to have some anyway." And Marge responds, "So am I. You only live once!" These are Child-Child messages, and Rose and Marge thus encourage each other to eat something extra. Again, they are kidding each other. The social level of communication has little to do with their actual intentions.

THE GALLOWS TRANSACTION

The gallows transaction is a special kind of ulterior transaction. Its superficial or social purpose is to entertain, to make human interaction more pleasurable, to provide a few laughs. Its deeper or psychological aim is to consolidate the I'm not OK position of the transaction's instigator, to provide him with a discount, to give him a social opportunity to dump on himself.

The name "gallows transaction" comes from the story of the man who was about to be hanged. He was offered a cigarette as a last pleasure before the trap was sprung. "No, thanks," he replied. I'm afraid of getting lung cancer." He laughs or smiles, and the audience also laughs or smiles. We presumably admire the person who can die laughing.

There are many examples of how overweight persons employ the gallows transaction. A wife comes home from a visit to her physician. The purpose of her visit was to discuss the fact that she has been gaining weight steadily for the past year. "What did he say?" her husband asks innocently. "He said, 'Open your mouth and say moo!'" quips the wife. "Ha, ha, ha!" And they both crack up.

A member of an overweight discussion group says, "My girlfriends tell me that I believe in a balanced diet—a cream puff in each hand. Ha, ha, ha!" "Ha, ha, ha!" responds the group.

Diana is having a between-meal piece of pie with a friend at a cafeteria shopping center. "These between-meal snacks are the pauses that *reflesh* me. Ha, ha, ha!" "Ha, ha, ha!" responds her friend.

Linda, a client in psychotherapy, tells her psychologist, "If I'm not overweight, then I'm certainly six inches too short. Ha, ha, ha!" "Ha, ha, ha!" responds her psychologist.

Donna, a member of an overweight discussion group, says,

"Every time I step on a scale, I'm reminded of one of President Roosevelt's famous phrases: A *gain*—and a *gain*—and a *gain*. Ha, ha, ha!" "Ha, ha, ha!" responds the group.

Sometimes the instigator of the gallows transaction isn't even clever. Lana, a member of one of my overweight discussion groups, told the group, "Last night the most hilarious thing happened. I got up in the middle of the night and I went to the refrigerator. I ate all the leftover chicken and half a loaf of bread in the dark by the kitchen sink. Ha, ha, ha!" "Ha, ha, ha!" responded the group dutifully. I asked Lana, "Do you think that maybe you're laughing on the outside and crying on the inside?" This question activated Lana's Adult, and she agreed that the idea contained in my question was correct.

On the social level, the gallows transaction is a Child-Child transaction.* The Child of person 1 tells a joke, and the Child of person 2 responds with laughter. The person telling the gag is obviously in his Child ego state. His eyes twinkle, he leans forward, and his face glows with merriment. If the listener responds in kind, the listener's Child has been activated. "Ha, ha, ha!" is a sound produced by the Child. However, at a deeper level, the gallows transaction is a Child-Parent transaction. The Adapted Child of person 1 is telling the critical Controlling Parent of person 2, "I'm not OK. Look at what a fool I am. Feel free to put me down and give me a psychological kick by laughing *at* me." The Controlling Parent of person 2 is all too happy to comply. "Yes," it says. "You're not OK. You are a fool. And I *am* laughing at you!" This transaction is diagrammed in Figure 6.

It should be clear by now that there is nothing really funny about the gallows transaction. It is a form of self-destructive behavior. Although superficially amusing, in the long run it downgrades one's self-image and adds to one's burden of de-

---

*I am aware that other writers on TA may specify different ego states as the active ones in this transaction. The development of social and psychological levels made here is based on my own counseling experience.

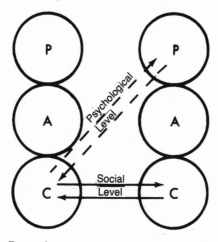

Person 1
"I ate all of the leftover chicken and a
half loaf of bread in the dark by the
kitchen sink. Ha, ha, ha!"

("Look at what a fool I am.")

Person 2
"Ha, ha, ha!"

("Yes, you are a fool!")

Figure 6. An example of a gallows transaction.

pression. Overweight people are laughed at enough without
inviting others to laugh at them.

So don't tell bad jokes and "funny" stories about your fat or
your eating transgressions. And don't contribute to another person's not OK feelings by laughing at such jokes. There is nothing
funny about fat. I know it all seems harmless enough. But this
"harmless" indulgence *keeps the overweight person from
thinking,* keeps him fixated at the Child level, where he can't
do anything for himself. When we laugh at fat, we laugh on the
gallows.

FREEDOM FROM FAT-MAKING TRANSACTIONS

In this chapter I have surveyed the principal kinds of fat-making transactions. The odds are high that you saw your own behavior reflected in some way in the descriptions and dialogues presented. If you did, you are now aware of the way you participate in these transactions. Awareness is the first step, and action is the second step toward breaking free from fixed communication patterns. In order to destroy the old molds, it is necessary to speak and act in new ways. Below is a list of *don'ts* and *dos* designed to help you achieve freedom from fat-making transactions. (There are more *don'ts* than *dos* because there seem to be more ways to go wrong in transactions than ways to go right.)

1. *Don't* initiate Parent-Parent complementary transactions in which you and another person give yourselves permission to overeat.
2. If you are an actual parent, *don't* initiate Parent-Parent complementary transactions in which you and your spouse indulge in fat-making criticisms in the presence of your children.
3. *Don't* initiate Child-Child complementary transactions in which you and another person enter your respective Child ego states, allowing the two of you to "throw caution to the winds" and eat impulsively.
4. If someone speaks down to you from his Parent, *don't* enter your Child. *Don't* play the role of good little boy or girl. *Don't* eat what the person playing the role of Parent says to eat just because he says it. *Don't* allow yourself to be intimidated by another person.
5. *Don't* initiate Child-Parent transactions in which you place yourself in the Child position and ask someone else for permission to indulge or overeat.

6. *Don't* participate in crossed transactions in which you and another person bicker and criticize each other about eating behavior. *Don't* exchange discounts. *Don't* collect angry brown stamps and trade them in for food you don't need.

7. *Don't* allow the discounts of other people to drive you more deeply into a negative life position. Eleanor Roosevelt once said, "No one can make you feel inferior without your consent." This is a thought well worth remembering when someone is trying to put you down.

8. *Don't* engage in ulterior fat-making transactions. *Don't* send social messages about eating that contradict your psychological messages. *Don't* be a faker, deceiving yourself and others.

9. *Don't* initiate gallows transactions in which you invite others to laugh at your eating follies. *Don't* invite discounts in this way.

10. *Don't* manipulate back if you feel that you are being manipulated. It isn't necessary to meet a con with a con. A hostess says, "I made this cake especially for you." Let's say that you resent the pressure and want to stand up for your rights. You're tempted to say, "My doctor says that I'm suffering from incipient hypoglycemia." This is an ulterior response. On the Adult-Adult level you seem to be giving information. But if the statement is *not* true, if the hostess detects that you are trying to razzle-dazzle her, you will be perceived as sending the psychological message "Stop bugging me!" This will be taken as a put-down, and it's hardly the best way to win friends and influence people. So what do you do?

11. *Do* assert yourself. If someone is pressuring you to eat, stand your ground. Say firmly from your Adult to the other person's Adult, "I'm full," or "I'm not hungry," or "I can't eat another bite." The psychologist Thomas Gordon refers to such statements as I-messages. They allow you to be firm without putting another person down.

I-messages are existential statements. They refer to your inner experience. As such, they can hardly be disputed. You may have to repeat an I-message more than once. But stick with it, and you'll get through to the other person's Adult.

12. *Do* initiate transactions from your Adult. Let's say that you are having lunch out with a co-worker. You're both eying the pie on display. Initiate a transaction from your Adult. Take the lead. Say, "That pie looks good. But I've had enough. I'm going to skip dessert." This is a communication arrow aimed straight at the other person's Adult. If the other person is also trying to resist the pie, the positive model you set will encourage him to follow your lead.

13. If another person addresses your Child from his Parent, *do* cross his transactional stimulus. Respond from your Adult, and send your message to his Adult. There is no reason to accept a one-down position. If you do, you will be participating in a fat-making Parent-Child transaction with you in the Child position. On the other hand, if you flip up to your own Parent and try to put the other person in a one-down position, you will be participating in a fat-making argumentative crossed transaction. Crossing the other person from your Parent to his Child is too harsh. The way out of this dilemma is a mild crossing, the crossing already described in which your Adult addresses the other person's Adult. This is the best way to deal with people who cast themselves in parental roles. What do you actually say? Again, we are back to the concept of I-messages. You just say, "I don't want any," or "Not now, thanks," or "I think I'll wait until later," or whatever indicates your actual feelings.

14. *Do* remember that it is within your power to end fat-making transactions. Understanding the transactional patterns described in this chapter, you can refuse to participate in them.

7

Games Fat People Play

"Stop playing games with me!"

"Do you really love me, or is this just a game you're playing?"

"He was playing a cat and mouse game with me."

"In the game of life, some are winners and some are losers."

In these quotations, the word "game" is used in familiar ways. We take it for granted that human beings engage each other in emotional contests associated with psychological gains and losses. In TA, however, "game" has a special meaning. It is a series of complementary ulterior transactions leading to a clear-cut, predictable outcome, an outcome with a dramatic quality.

The basic elements in a game are a con, a gimmick, a switch, a crossup, and a payoff. A *con* consists of a social message and a psychological message. The agent or instigator of the game is dishonest in that his social message is a cover for his psychological message. A *gimmick* is a psychological weakness of some sort on the part of the respondent or second player, providing a ready way for the con to take hold. If the con plays on a fear, a wish, an attitude, or a mood of the respondent, the respondent will be easily hooked by the con. The respondent thus becomes what we know by such slang terms as a mark, sucker, patsy, dupe, pushover, or fall guy. A *switch* takes place when the agent turns the tables on the respondent in some way. A *crossup* is what Berne calls "a moment of confusion" on the part of the mark. He is briefly puzzled, trying to figure out what happened to him. A *payoff* is the collection by both players of either good feelings (gold stamps) or bad feelings (brown stamps). The aim, of course, of the transactional analysis of games is to free us from their tyranny.

THE PLAYERS

The concept of games in TA assumes the interactions of at least two people, the agent and the respondent. As they play, the agent and the respondent adopt social roles. These are poses or fronts at the social level designed to contribute to the ulterior aims of the game. The two basic roles are the Persecutor and the Victim. These roles can be quickly switched during the progress of the game, a Victim becoming a Persecutor and a Persecutor becoming a Victim.

Three-handed games require an additional role: the Rescuer. On the social level, the Rescuer takes the position that he is "trying to help." On the psychological level, the Rescuer usually has ulterior aims of his own. A real rescuer should be distinguished from a Rescuer. When capitalized, Rescuer is a role in a game. A Rescuer fosters the dependency needs of the Victim and interferes with his potentialities for self-sufficient behavior. A real rescuer helps a Victim to grow, to depend on his own psychological resources. A real rescuer breaks up game patterns.

It is also possible to speak of multihanded games, games involving four or more persons. However, the extra persons play only peripheral roles. They are merely the pawns of the principal players, and it only confuses a game analysis to be concerned with the contributions of the "bit actors." In the analysis of fat-making games presented in this chapter, the focus of attention will be on the agent and the respondent.

WHY DO PEOPLE PLAY GAMES?

Before we explore some of the actual games fat people play, let us ask: Why do people play games? Here are the principal reasons:

1. They play games to satisfy their structure hunger. Game-playing is something to do when there is nothing better to do.
2. They play games to exchange strokes. All transactions have stroke value. Negative strokes are better than no strokes at all. Sometimes being put down is better than being ignored. Thus games deal with the general problem of recognition hunger.
3. They play games to collect psychological stamps. People seeking bad feelings collect brown stamps; those seeking good feelings collect gold stamps.
4. They play games to consolidate a life position. If, for example, a person is in the I'm not OK—You're OK life position, the outcome of the game helps him to prove that his life position is correct. Although it is more common to play a game to consolidate a life position, there are times when this is not the case. If, for example, a person is in the I'm not OK—You're OK life position, the outcome of certain games may leave him one up, with a gold stamp. When this happens, playing the game provides him with a bit of relief from the burden of his life position.

"COMPULSIVE EATER," OR "SOMEONE TO WATCH OVER ME"

The fat-making game called "Compulsive Eater," or "Someone to Watch Over Me," requires the social roles of Compulsive

Eater and Watchdog. The Compulsive Eater adopts the pose that he is neurotic, that overeating is the symptom of an underlying psychological illness. In TA the compulsive eater or the "foodaholic" is not a "sick" person who "has" a psychological problem that must be cured. On the contrary, Compulsive Eater is a role he has decided to play in a game. He plays the role because it offers him certain psychological satisfactions. The role is played from the I'm not OK—You're OK position. The Watchdog takes the stance that he can successfully supervise and control the behavior of the Compulsive Eater through authoritarian tactics. The role is played from the I'm OK—You're not OK position.

Audrey and Robert B. are the players in a typical game of "Compulsive Eater." When Audrey was nineteen years old she was about twenty pounds overweight. She dieted strenuously, and lost the weight in five weeks. She met Robert a few months later. After a whirlwind courtship, they were married. Robert was very much in love with his slim 110-pound bride. However, to his dismay, Audrey began to gain weight only a few months after the marriage. Within ten weeks she regained the twenty pounds she had lost before meeting Robert. Soon the game of Compulsive Eater started, and they have played it many times. Here are the typical moves in a round of "Compulsive Eater" as played by Audrey and Robert:

The con. Audrey complains about how fat she is getting. At the social level her Adapted Child pleads with Robert's Controlling Parent, "Help me lose some weight. Be my guardian. I need someone to watch over me. Stop me when you see me take second helpings. I can't do it on my own. Help me bolster my will power." The con is ulterior because at the psychological level Audrey is seeking justification for her overeating. Her Adapted Child is saying to his Adapted Child, "You can't help me. I'm a compulsive eater."

The gimmick. The gimmick is Robert's need to be in control, his wish to exercise power over another person. At the social level his Controlling Parent responds to the plea of her Adapted

Child with, "OK, I'll watch what you're doing. And I'll let you know when I see you eating too much." At the psychological level his Adapted Child admits to her Adapted Child, "I know I can't really help you. When you overeat, I feel helpless."

The switch. Audrey diets compulsively for a few days. When she begins to eat too much in Robert's presence, he sends her warning signs, and she immediately curtails her eating. However, after a few days she pulls the switch. She goes on a binge while Robert is at work, and leaves many telltale signs in the kitchen. The idea is to let him know that she has quite definitely cheated and blown her diet.

The crossup. When Robert comes home, he sees the dirty dishes on the kitchen counter, notes the fact that most of yesterday's roast is missing from the refrigerator, and observes the empty nut jar in the trash can. He acts befuddled and bewildered, as if he can't really believe what has happened. Soon he expresses to Audrey his sense of frustration and anger, his disgust with her behavior.

The payoff. Audrey is hurt and depressed. She collects a brown stamp and consolidates her I'm not OK—You're OK life position. Robert feels righteous indignation. He collects a gold stamp and consolidates his I'm OK—You're not OK life position.

In the case of Audrey and Robert the game is complicated by the interference of Robert's mother, who plays the role of Rescuer. She supplies Audrey with new diets, advice on eating, and appropriate moral lectures. None of this helps Audrey. It is clear that Robert's mother is not a legitimate rescuer, but a person playing the role of Rescuer for her own satisfaction. She feels superior to Audrey, never having had a weight problem herself, and she only compounds Audrey's inferiority feelings. On a social level, Robert's mother is on Audrey's side. "I am only trying to help." But on a psychological level, she is Robert's ally, informing Audrey in various ways that she is not OK fat.

I consider the game of "Compulsive Eater" the most common game fat people play. As I have said before, it is my observation that most overweight persons are in the I'm not OK—

You're OK life position. It is easy to see how a person who is playing the role of Compulsive Eater might con a physician or a friend into playing the game. Thus there are a number of variations that can be played on the basic game.

Many games do not have a Rescuer. It is not an essential game role. In the games yet to be discussed, I focus on the roles of the two principal players.

"FAT RECLUSE," OR "I NEVER GO ANYWHERE"

The two principal roles in "Fat Recluse," or "I Never Go Anywhere" are the Fat Recluse and the Nice Guy. The game is most commonly played by a wife taking on the role of Fat Recluse and a husband taking on the role of Nice Guy, so I will present it from that point of view. The Fat Recluse adopts the pose that she is stuck at home primarily because of her husband's neglect. For example, she may not be able to drive, there is no convenient public transportation, she has no friends who can chauffeur her around, her married children live far away and don't care about her, and the places where she shops are not within easy walking distance. The role is played from the I'm not OK—You're not OK position. The Nice Guy adopts the position that he will take his wife anywhere she wants to go. He claims that he takes her out often. Naturally, he works and some evenings he is tired. But he strives to please her. He agrees that her complaints are legitimate, and tries to accommodate himself to them. His role is played from the I'm not OK —You're OK position.

Brenda and Arnold L. are the players in a typical game of "Fat Recluse." Fifty-five years old, Brenda feels that she is "over the hill." Her children are grown. She mourns the attractive young woman she once was. Demoralized, she eats indiscriminately without any attempt at self-restriction. On a typical day Brenda gets out of bed around ten o'clock. Her husband leaves for work at seven, and he fixes his own breakfast. She is faced with a day of utter loneliness. Very few friends call or visit, and she initiates no contacts. All she looks forward to is watching television and eating. Most of the day she wears a dirty bathrobe, making minimal efforts to groom herself. The house is a mess. It needs to be dusted and vacuumed. But Brenda spends most of her time hypnotized by game shows and soap operas. Around four o'clock she usually manages to get up enough energy to put on some sort of dress and start a meal for her husband. She has not lost complete touch with the reality of her responsibilities, but almost.

Brenda eats eight or nine times in the hours between when she gets up, and 6 P.M., when her husband gets home. A half hour after breakfast she is eating a doughnut. An hour before lunch she is eating a candy bar. An hour after lunch she may eat a whole bag of potato chips. If there are chain smokers, then Brenda must be a chain eater. Finishing a bag of potato chips may suggest to her that she eat a bowl of peanuts. Finishing the bowl of peanuts may suggest to her that she dig into a box of cookies. Brenda weighs over 250 pounds, and she gains a little more weight each year. (She is five feet two inches tall.)

Arnold works at a factory on an assembly line. He has held the same job for twenty years. He is a thin little man, a plodder, a "nice guy" to all who know him. He seems to be mystified by his wife's behavior, and has accepted her viewpoint that her problems are largely his fault. Here are the typical moves in a round of "Fat Recluse" as played by Brenda and Arnold:

The con. Brenda complains about being stuck in the house. At the social level her Controlling Parent says to his Adapted Child, "You never take me anywhere. I'm stuck home all the time. I want to get out of the house." The con is ulterior because at the psychological level Brenda is seeking justification for staying at home and hiding from the world. Her Adapted Child is saying to his Controlling Parent, "I want to hide. I want to hide in the house. I want to hide behind my fat. Help me do it."

The gimmick. The gimmick is Arnold's need to help his wife hide. He is ashamed of her, and does not enjoy being seen in public places with her. At the social level his Adapted Child meekly responds to her Controlling Parent by saying, "I'll take you anywhere you want to go." At the psychological level his Controlling Parent says to her Adapted Child, "I'll help you hide. I don't like to be seen with you."

The switch. Arnold agrees to take Brenda to a shopping mall on a Sunday afternoon. They have only been at the mall for a short time when Brenda suddenly declares, "You're not having a good time. I can tell. You're not being nice to me. Let's go home!"

The crossup. Arnold is bewildered. Here he is doing what she wants him to do, he is trying hard to please her, and suddenly out of nowhere she complains and wants to go home. He must be doing something wrong, but what? In fact, he *is* doing something wrong. He doesn't see the sad expression on his face when he is out with her. Arnold agrees to take Brenda home, and the afternoon outing is quickly terminated.

The payoff. Brenda feels worthless, that she has no value as a human being. She collects a brown stamp and consolidates her I'm not OK—You're not OK position. Arnold feels incompetent. He also collects a brown stamp, and consolidates his I'm not OK —You're OK position.

"IF YOU LOVED ME FOR ME"

In a typical version of the game called "If You Loved Me for Me," a wife plays the role of Unloved Little Girl and a husband plays the role of Daddy Coldblood. (Of course the roles can be reversed, in which case they would be called Unloved Little Boy and Mama Coldblood.) The role of Unloved Little Girl requires that the female play the part of a supplicant looking for love. The role is played from the I'm not OK—You're OK position. The role of Daddy Coldblood requires that the male play the part of one who graciously bestows love upon the woman. The role is played from the I'm OK—You're not OK position.

Here is a typical round of "If You Loved Me for Me" as it is played by Laura and Edgar G., a married couple:

The con. It is evening. Laura is reading a detective story and Edgar is watching a baseball game on television. Laura is feeling sorry for herself and somewhat neglected. She puts down her book and decides to intrude upon Edgar's preoccupation with the game. At the social level her Adapted Child asks in a slightly whining voice of his Nurturing Parent, "Do you still love me?" At the psychological level there is a second message from her Adapted Child aimed at his Controlling Parent, saying, "I know you don't love me. If you did, it wouldn't make any difference that I'm forty pounds overweight. I'm the same person I always was. There's just more of me to love."

The gimmick. The gimmick is Edgar's need to let Laura know that she is not loved for herself, that her complaints make no sense to him. At the social level he tries to reassure her. So his Nurturing Parent says to her Adapted Child, "Of course I love you." But a false note creeps into his voice. And his Controlling Parent says to her Adapted Child, "I'm not so sure. You're being so fat is really beginning to turn me off."

The switch. Laura detects the false note in Edgar's voice, translates his code, and feels put down. Edgar expects her to act reassured by his words. But she unexpectedly blurts out in emotional pain, "I don't feel loved!"

The crossup. Edgar wonders what happened. He reassured her that he still loves her, and she turns on him! What do women want anyhow? They can't be satisfied!

The payoff. Laura feels more unloved than ever. She collects a brown stamp and consolidates her I'm not OK—You're OK life position. Later in the evening she trades in the brown stamp for a snack. Edgar's feeling is a kind of cold-blooded disgust with Laura for conning him into playing her game and expecting him to love her on an unconditional basis. He thinks her emotional demands are unfair. Thus he collects a gold stamp and consolidates his I'm OK—You're not OK position.

"FAT CLOWN," OR "WATCH ME
MAKE A FOOL OF MYSELF"

The two principal social roles in "Fat Clown," or "Watch Me Make a Fool of Myself" are the Fat Clown and the Spectator. The part of Fat Clown is played by someone who is willing to be laughed at in order to obtain an ulterior aim. The role is played from the I'm not OK—You're OK position. The part of Spectator is played by someone who is willing to laugh at the Fat Clown's folly. The role is played from the I'm OK—You're not OK position. Here is a typical round of "Fat Clown" as it is played by Oliver and Alice G.:

The con. Oliver and Alice are eating dinner out at a buffet restaurant that has an eat-all-you-want policy. Oliver has had one helping of roast beef and two helpings of fried chicken. His Adult asks her Adult, "Do you think I should go back for a fourth helping?" On the surface, the message appears to be a rational request for an opinion. However, at the psychological level he is seeking attention. His Adapted Child asks her Controlling Parent, "Do you want to watch me make a fool of myself?"

The gimmick. At the social level Alice's Adult responds to his question with: "It's probably not a good idea." But she wishes to laugh at him, and this is the gimmick. So she manages to communicate at the psychological level from her Controlling Parent to his Adapted Child: "Sure. I need some laughs today."

The switch. Oliver has his fourth helping, and the two partners in their own way manage to get some kicks out of the fact that Oliver has made a hog out of himself. The switch takes place later at a movie. Halfway through the film Oliver complains of indigestion. He insists that they leave so that he can go home and take some baking soda. He blames Alice for his misery. "Why did you let me do it?" he demands. "Why did you let me go for a fourth helping?"

The crossup. Alice is perplexed by Oliver's accusation. She protests her innocence. "But I said it probably wasn't a good idea to go back for the fourth helping!"

The payoff. Oliver feels that he is not to blame for his intemperate behavior. He projects the blame into Alice and collects a gold stamp, obtaining a bit of relief* from his I'm not OK—You're OK position. Alice feels guilty. Somehow she ruined the evening. She collects a brown stamp, obtaining a bit of relief from her I'm OK—You're not OK position.

"LOOK HOW HARD I'VE TRIED TO LOSE WEIGHT"

"Look How Hard I've Tried to Lose Weight" is a version of a TA game known as "Why Don't You—Yes But." The two principal social roles are the Seeker and the Sage. The role of Seeker calls for a person to ask for information or advice about losing weight. The role is played from the I'm not OK—You're OK position. The role of Sage calls for a person who is willing to dispense wisdom glibly. The role is played from the I'm OK—You're not OK position. Here is a typical round of "Look How Hard I've Tried to Lose Weight" as it is played by two acquaintances, Barbara N. and Marge O.:

The con. Barbara plays the role of Seeker. At the social level her Adult says to Marge's Adult, "I've tried everything to lose weight. And nothing works. Do you have any good ideas that might help me?" At the psychological level Barbara's Adapted Child is saying to Marge's Controlling Parent, "Look how hard I've tried to lose weight. I want to be excused for being fat. It's not my fault."

The gimmick. Marge plays the role of Sage. She needs to demonstrate her superior store of wisdom. At the social level

---

*Again, I would like to point out that in most TA books, game outcomes are interpreted in terms of how they serve to consolidate the life positions of the players. Here (and in several other games in this chapter) the payoffs are presented in terms of *relief* provided from life positions because this is how I have observed the games to work out in actual practice.

her Adult says to Barbara's Adult, "Why don't you try a hypnotist? I read an article that said it really works." On the psychological level her Controlling Parent is saying to Barbara's Adapted Child, "You see, my dear. There *is* a way to lose weight. I have just shown you a road that you didn't know about. I will not excuse you for being fat."

The switch. Barbara pulls the switch by responding to Marge's suggestion: "Yes, but I tried hypnosis two years ago. It didn't really do me any good. I lost weight at first, but I gained it all back."

The crossup. Marge experiences a moment of confusion, but may fairly rapidly come back with another bright idea. And a second round of the game may be quickly played.

The payoff. Barbara feels smug. She has "proved" that her case is hopeless. She collects a gold stamp, obtaining a bit of relief from her I'm not OK—You're OK position. Marge feels like a fool instead of the Sage. She collects a brown stamp, obtaining a bit of relief from her I'm OK—You're not OK position.

"Look How Hard I've Tried to Lose Weight" is often played in therapy groups. The Seeker often cons more than one person into playing the role of Sage. Many suggestions are made:

"Why don't you try a low-calorie diet?"

"Why don't you try a low-carbohydrate diet?"

"Why don't you try fasting?"

"Why don't you try those new shots they're giving?"

"Why don't you try thyroid pills?"

"Why don't you try exercising more?"

"Why don't you try acupuncture?"

The Seeker can easily pull a switch on any of these suggestions with: "Yes, but . . ." The therapist may allow the game to continue for a time. At some point he may consider it instructive to blow the whistle on the game and point out to the Adult ego states of the players the ulterior aspects of the game.

"HELP ME LOSE WEIGHT," DR. DODO

The game called "Help Me Lose Weight, Dr. Dodo" requires a person playing the role of Compulsive Eater and a psychotherapist playing the role of Exalted Wizard. Let's make the assumption that the Compulsive Eater is a female and the Exalted Wizard is a male. The Compulsive Eater adopts the pose that she needs help to lose weight, that she knows she is neurotic, and that she is convinced that some form of psychotherapy is the answer to her problems. She plays the role from the I'm not OK—You're OK position. The Exalted Wizard adopts the pose that he is an expert, that he cures patients of their problems, that he uses the latest methods. He plays the role from the I'm OK—You're not OK position. Here is a typical round of "Help Me, Dr. Dodo" as it is played by Lois F. and her therapist, Dr. Z.

The con. Lois goes to see Dr. Z. for the first visit. She tells him that her close friend, Sally, was greatly helped by him. At the social level her Adapted Child asks his Nurturing Parent for help. "I need you, Doctor." At the psychological level her Rebellious Child is saying to his Controlling Parent, "You can't help me. I'm going to show you that you don't know everything. I'll take the wind out of your sails!"

The gimmick. At the social level Dr. Z's Nurturing Parent reassures her Adapted Child. "We'll use the latest methods. I think we can expect good results." The gimmick is Dr. Z's excessive need to be a competent therapist. He is uptight about his expertise. And this is why he comes across as a stuffed shirt. He plays the role of Exalted Wizard in order to mask his doubts. At the psychological level his Controlling Parent says to her Rebellious Child, "I'll show you I *do* have the answer to your problems."

The switch. For a few weeks all goes well. Lois hangs on every word in therapy sessions, "makes progress," and begins to lose weight. Then she pulls the switch. She comes for a therapy session in tears. She reveals that she went on a binge during the week, that she has gained weight, and that she has lost all self-control. Dr. Z. is, of course, Lois's mark. He has been set up for a fall. The psychological message emanating from her lament is: "You're stupid. You're not Dr. Z. You're Dr. Dodo!"

The crossup. The real dodo bird *(Didus ineptus)* was a wingless fowl found in the island of Mauritius. Like Dr. Z., it allowed itself to be clubbed on the head. After his psychological clubbing, Dr. Z. has a bit of trouble collecting his wits. "I can't understand it," he thinks. "I used the latest techniques."

The payoff. Lois is victorious. She has demonstrated to the Exalted Wizard that he's not so great after all. As she leaves his office that day, she is exalted. She collects a gold stamp, obtaining a bit of relief from her I'm not OK—You're OK position. Dr. Z. feels chagrined. He collects a brown stamp, obtaining a bit of relief from his I'm OK—You're not OK position.

I know only too well what it is to be cast in the role of Dr. Dodo. In my early years of counseling overweight people, I had in individual therapy a young woman named Sharon G. At that time I was enamored with the behavioral approach to obesity, and had worked out a set of behavior modification techniques for compulsive-impulsive eaters. I presented these techniques to Sharon, explaining patiently how she could apply them. She was intelligent, understood the instructions, and employed the techniques for a time. Then came the switch. She began overeating, refused to use the techniques, and became very emotional. In subsequent discussions, it turned out that she had had great resistance to the techniques from the beginning. She said, "It's like you've got this really neat system, and I want to shoot it down." Coming into counseling in the role of Compulsive Eater, and feeling in a one-down I'm not OK—You're OK position, Sharon had a great need to turn the tables on the Exalted Wizard—show him that maybe he wasn't so OK after all. And she succeeded. Dr. Dodo took a flop.

Fortunately, Sharon and I were able to figure out what was

going on. We ended the game and put our relationship on a new basis. I stopped presenting the behavior modification techniques as Great Ideas. Instead I offered them as notions to discuss, consider, and evaluate together. Our transactions became Adult-Adult without an ulterior side. She used some of the techniques, modified some, and rejected some. In a short time she lost weight and she has kept it off. As you can see from reading this book, I am not a strict behavior therapist—that is, a therapist who analyzes and modifies behavioral patterns. I find it necessary first to know my clients as persons, to explore with them their thoughts and feelings. And only after I have shown them how to avoid self-defeating roles in fat-making games do I apply behavior modification techniques.

FAT-MAKING WOODEN LEGS

Wooden legs are often integral parts of games. The term *wooden leg*, from Berne's game of the same name, is sometimes used in TA to identify a weak, self-indulgent excuse for a particular behavior. As already noted, a person with a real wooden leg might say, "I can't dance—what do you expect of someone with a wooden leg!" Another person, with a real wooden leg, might say, "I *can* dance in spite of my wooden leg!" Overweight persons often develop wooden legs, allowing for superficial justifications for their unnecessary eating. TA takes a somewhat cynical view of an overweight person's best wooden leg. The idea is to help you catch yourself in the act, to help you identify a wooden leg. Let's now examine some of the more important wooden legs.

"Alice in Fatland"

The basic theme of "Alice in Fatland" is: "I can't help overeating. Everywhere I go there is food, food, food! How can someone with my poor will power resist the constant pounding we get from TV commercials, magazine advertising, supermarket displays, and the signs on fast-food places?" The person playing the role of Alice sees herself (or himself) the way Alice did in Wonderland. All these crazy characters were talking to her all the time, telling her what to do. The Mad Hatter was saying one thing, the Cheshire cat something else. Alice felt that she was going in mental circles, that she was scarcely able to direct her own behavior. Similarly, a modern-day Alice may feel that it is *them* that make her eat, that she is the victim of psychological forces larger than she is. Of course, most overweight persons are suggestible and overly responsive to both food and food-related cues. Alice in Fatland is a wooden leg only for those who use their awareness of this tendency as a cop-out. It is the Child that whines, "I can't help myself. They keep shoving food at me." The Adult can say, "I will not have food shoved down my throat. I will not be told what to do. I can say no. I am not a hypnotized subject. I can listen to my own inner voice instead of external voices."

Gourmet

The person playing the role of Gourmet justifies his behavior by saying, "I can't help it. I just love to eat. I love to sample different dishes, to experiment with different restaurants. How do you expect a gourmet to be slim?" If you watch the fat Gourmet's behavior, you will see him eating rapidly—hardly tasting his food! In fact, he is anything but a gourmet. A real gourmet is discriminating, takes modest portions, pauses between bites, pays close attention to the taste and texture of the food, and may clear his mouth with a sip of water or wine. The role-playing Gourmet gobbles up everything in sight, takes seconds, shoves one mouthful on top of another, and swallows without tasting. If you role-play the Gourmet, try to catch yourself in the act. Blow the whistle on your self-indulgent pattern and ask yourself from your Adult, "Who am I kidding?"

"Dumbo"

The fat person playing the role of Dumbo acts stupid. The basic pose is: "I'm fat and dumb. I don't know anything about correct eating, calories, or nutrition. What can you expect of a dope like me?" Such people often act quite silly when talking about their weight problems. One of my overweight clients, Susan E., giggled as she told me that she drank eight big bottles of a popular soft drink a day. When I mentioned the high sugar and caloric contents of the drinks, she professed astonishment. "Gee, I didn't know they were that fattening!" Subsequent discussions revealed that this was just an act. Susan was pretending even to herself that she was ignorant, pulling the wool over her own eyes.

The Dumbo act comes straight out of the Child. Just as actual children will play dumb in order to provide an excuse for their failures, so will the overweight adolescent or adult take on the role of Dumbo to provide a superficial explanation for his weight problem. A person in the habit of playing the role of Dumbo needs to learn to say to himself out of his Adult, "Who am I kidding? I know how fattening my favorite treats are. I'm not dumb. I'm smarter than I'm giving myself credit for."

"My Destiny"

"My Destiny" is basically a wooden leg in which the person playing the role of Destined One takes the position that he is the Victim of Fate. The underlying theme is: "It's my destiny to be fat. Fat runs in my family. My mother and father were fat. My grandparents were fat. I probably inherited fat-making genes. Everything I eat goes to fat. There's just nothing I can do about it." All this may sound fairly plausible, but its phony character is revealed by examining some of these assumptions. The Destined One might ask himself from his Adult, "Were my parents and other relatives fat because of heredity or because of eating styles? Does fat run in our genes or in our traditional family eating patterns? Is it really true that everything I eat goes to fat? When was the last time I made a realistic estimate of my total caloric intake for a day or a week? Do I really believe at the deepest level of my being that I'm fated to be fat?"

"Junk Food Junkie"

The Junk Food Junkie is saying to himself and to the world, "I'm addicted to junk foods, and I can't help it. I know they're bad for me, but I love to stuff myself with greasy hamburgers, hot dogs, fries, shakes, doughnuts, candy bars, ice cream cones, tacos, cookies, and all the rest. I crave foods loaded with sugar or grease the way a drug addict craves a fix."

His "addiction" is his wooden leg, his excuse for his eating behavior. The Junkie has cast himself in the role of Victim, his Persecutors being the marketers of junk foods. Thus the responsibility is transferred from the self to those who would control the self.

Junkie is an illegitimate role because it is unlikely that there is any organic-physiological basis for the idea that one is "hooked" or truly addicted to junk foods. The junk-food habit is a learned habit, not really comparable to big Habits, such as heroin addiction. (Even that Habit has important learned components.) A learned habit can be unlearned. The role of Junk Food Junkie is countered by plugging into the Adult and asking oneself a series of reality-oriented questions: "How did I get started on junk foods? How can I avoid them? What can I substitute for junk foods? Do I really have to have junk foods to survive? If I didn't eat junk foods for one week, how would I feel physically?" (If you have a high sugar intake, you might experience some slight "withdrawal" symptoms for a few days. However, most persons suffer only mild organic discomfort while cutting down on the sugar in their diet.) If you are a Junk Food

Junkie, take a hard look at the role you are playing. Think of it as a false act and a wooden leg, and recognize that you have a choice to play or not play the role.

ENDING THE GAMES

It is, of course, to your advantage to end fat-making games, and to throw away your fat-making wooden legs. Eric Berne believed that for every game there is an *antithesis* or a "stopper," a move or set of moves that will end the game. This is a very hopeful point of view, and I share it. What is required is that you learn to enter your Adult when you're tempted to play a game. From your Adult, you evaluate your behavior in a realistic way. Under these conditions, it is possible to modify your behavior in a constructive direction. Here are some guidelines that will help you to bring fat-making games to a halt:

1. Avoid ulterior transactions. Remember that an ulterior transaction has both a social level and a psychological level. The social level is the "nice" cover for more meaningful messages emanating from the psychological level. Thus ulterior transactions are deceptive, tend to be manipulative, and contribute to fat-making games.
2. Identify your games and the roles you play in them. Give each a name, such as Compulsive Eater—or a new name for games you discover yourself. Naming the game externalizes it, which helps you to dissociate yourself from it.
3. Remember that it takes two to play a game. However, it takes only one person to stop a game. It is your choice. You can refuse to play games.
4. Refuse to play the role of Victim. Recognize that it is an illegitimate role, that it is perpetuated by your wooden legs, that it arises from patterns of emotional self-indulgence and self-deception.
5. Refuse to play the role of Persecutor, a role in which you

contribute to another person's obesity. Persecutor is also a self-indulgent illegitimate role.

6. Refuse to play the role of Rescuer, a role in which you are duped into becoming either the Victim's patsy or the Persecutor's ally. It is difficult to be a real rescuer, and it is all too easy to be tricked into the illegitimate role of Rescuer.

7. Remember that the master key to ending games is knowing how to bring your Adult into your thoughts and actions. It is the use of your Adult that can set you free from the dead-end, self-destructive patterns of fat-making games and wooden legs.

In *Awareness* by Gestalt therapist John O. Stevens, there appears the following statement: "A great deal of the weakness, stupidity, and craziness in the world is not real; it is playing weak, playing stupid, and playing crazy."* I share Stevens's viewpoint. That's why I believe that you really can use your Adult to stop playing illegitimate roles in fat-making games. It really *is* possible to break free from self-defeating patterns!

GAME-FREE LIVING

After games, what? What is game-free living like? Game-free living contributes, of course, to fat-free living. What's more, a game-free life is a life with two wonderful attributes: *autonomy* and *intimacy*. Autonomy is the inner realization that you are in charge of your own life, that you are "the master of your fate, the captain of your soul." The tremendous popularity of a book such as *Jonathan Livingston Seagull,* an allegory about a bird that soars free of conventional restraints, reveals the depth of the craving for autonomy. We admire Jonathan because he owns his own existence. Like Jonathan, the autonomous person is capable of self-direction—he rises above circumstances that

*John O. Stevens, *Awareness: Exploring, Experimenting, Experiencing* (Bantam, 1973), p. 145.

would undermine the validity of his inner being. The autonomous person does not jerk like a puppet on a string when others try to manipulate him. He does not eat because a spouse, a friend, or a situation presses his Child button. He and he alone decides when to eat, where to eat, what to eat, and how much to eat. Unlike the passive person—the eating puppet—the autonomous person initiates his own behavior.

Intimacy may be defined as *emotional closeness* with another person. The game-free relationship is characterized by genuine respect between two people. They value each other, see each other's point of view, express feelings honestly, and do not feel that one person possesses the other person. From the point of view of weight control, the great value of such a relationship resides in the fact that it is a rich source of nurturing strokes. As I have indicated previously, excessive eating is often a response to a big stroke hunger in the Adapted Child. The person whose stroke hunger is satisfied is much less likely to seek food for psychological-emotional nourishment.

These are the benefits to be derived from game-free living. They are great, indeed. However, it is certainly too idealistic, and quite unrealistic, to expect that persons in the habit of playing games will give up games overnight. The transition from a game-playing life to a game-free life is gradual, a growth process, and requires effort. Nonetheless, the rewards of game-free living are definitely worth the effort you invest. As you go forward in life, set your sights on the twin stars of autonomy and intimacy.

8

Fat-Making Scripts

According to TA theory, many people decide on a life plan, or "script," sometime during their childhood or early adolescence. Thus a script in TA is an inner directive that determines the course and outcome of a person's life. Although the script or life plan was the result of a conscious decision made by the Child ego state in one's early years, the script in the adult years is usually operating at an unconscious level. By bringing the script to the surface, a decision made by the Child on an emotional basis can be reexamined, reevaluated, and undecided (or redecided) by the logical capacities of the inner Adult. TA firmly asserts that early decisions are reversible. Thus there *is hope* for persons who have adopted self-destructive life scripts.

The concept of a script in TA is similar to the concept of a *life style* as presented by the depth psychologist Alfred Adler. Adler, a pioneer in personality theory, believed that children adopt a life style at a very early age. This is their way of coping with the world. The life style may have a dominant theme such as depression, inferiority, egocentricity, and striving. It determines to a large extent the individual's personal destiny and the goals he sets for himself in life.

Does everyone have a script? No, not everyone. It should be remembered that the insights about human nature derived from TA and depth psychology are based primarily on the study of troubled persons. It would probably be appropriate to say that most troubled persons have what might be called a script or a self-defeating life style. A fully functioning person has instead a flexible life plan determined by the Adult. There is nothing compulsive about it; it can be revised and modified as circumstances require. However, a person behaving out of a script is *programmed*. Like a robot, he stumbles through life without sufficient awareness of the need to think, to grow, and to change. Again, TA offers the hope that persons who are living scripted lives can break free and become autonomous.

There is a close relationship between life positions, games, and scripts. The basic life position (for example, I'm not OK—You're OK) to a large extent determines the script the Child will adopt. Games tell us what to do with our time. We seem to have a time-structure hunger. We want to know how we are going to spend the day or the week. Thus games structure time for the short run. Scripts also have a time-structuring function. They tell us how we are going to spend our years and our lives. Thus scripts structure time for the long run.

We can, of course, structure time without the crutches of games and scripts. How we spend our time can be determined by Adult decisions. Playing games and living out scripts represents a nonthinking form of time structuring determined by the Child.

Our reward for breaking free of scripts will be the same as our reward for breaking free of games: a better life—a life with the twin attributes of autonomy and intimacy. A script-free life will be fat-free. For the person who lives a script-free existence has little need to eat for strokes, to eat out of anger, or to abuse food in other ways.

OF HEXES AND CURSES

At the social level, most parents want only the best for their children. They thus send many "nice" messages to their children, such as: "Be beautiful," "Be good-looking," "Make a lot of money," "Get married to a wonderful person," "Be slim," "Eat properly," "Get plenty of exercise," and so forth. Parents who mean what they say, whose communications have no ulterior content, are referred to in TA as jolly green giants and fairy godmothers. If your father was a jolly green giant and your mother was a fairy godmother, they came on straight with you; they raised you primarily from their own Nurturing Parent ego states. In TA terminology, you were born OK—a natural prince or princess—and your parents were able to foster and preserve your OK feelings. With such parents, you would probably not have a weight problem or a fat-making script. (If you have any script at all—and you may not—it is a "winning" script, a script that says it is OK to enjoy life and attain constructive goals.)

Few of us are fortunate enough to have had jolly green giants and fairy godmothers for parents. It is quite likely that your parents had resentments, frustrations, troubles, internal conflicts, compulsions, rigidities, prejudices, hang-ups, and not OK feelings of their own. If so, they probably inflicted these upon you via their own Child ego states. What they *told* you to do from their Parent ego states was one thing. What they *programmed* you to do from their Child ego states was quite another. At a psychological level, a child is often "hexed" and "cursed" with destructive messages. These destructive messages are sometimes spoken in words; however, they are often sent in more subtle ways with body language, actions, expressions, and tone of voice.

Examples of hexes and curses are: "You're ugly," "You're dumb," "You'll never amount to anything," "You're selfish," "You'll grow up to be a bum," "You have no respect for us," "You're a troublemaker," "You're sloppy," "You'll get fat when you get married," "You'll get fat after you have babies," "You can't stick to a diet," "You have no will power," "You're never going to lose your baby fat," "Fat runs in our family," "You were a fat baby, a fat child, and you'll be fat all your life," "No one will really ever love you because you're too fat," and so forth.

Parents who hex their children in these ways are referred to in TA as ogre fathers and witch mothers. The ogre father and the witch mother represent the Child ego states of the parents. It is the actual child's reaction from his own Child ego state that determines the script. The script is thus decided upon by a person too young to make a responsible, reality-oriented life plan. Nonetheless, it is made, and it often sticks for years or for life.

The basic script decision made by the child is called the *script protocol,* a rough draft of what life will be like when one grows up. The script protocol can be very brief: "Nobody loves me. Nobody will ever love me. I'm going to be a very lonely person all my life." The final version of the script, the version the person actually lives out in adulthood, is called the *shooting script.* The shooting script is usually replete with a cast of stock characters: a spouse, children, in-laws, friends, enemies. These individuals will provide the dramatic value required by a particular shooting script. Many of the characters are *picked* by the scriptwriter for their capacity to play certain roles. For example, if Cathy has decided that "Nobody loves me," she will agree to marry only a man her Child confirms: "Yes, you can marry him. He will not love you. He will prove that the script decision is correct."

In my counseling work with overweight people, I have detected three main kinds of fat-making scripts. These are: (1) the "Looking for Love" script, (2) the "Everybody Look at Me" script, and (3) the "Going Crazy" script. All are self-defeating and self-destructive in the long run. Let us now explore their individual characteristics.

THE "LOOKING FOR LOVE" SCRIPT

The "Looking for Love" script is lived out of the I'm not OK —You're OK life position. It is the most common of the three basic fat-making scripts, and it represents a big stroke hunger.

Individuals with "Looking for Love" scripts have large Adapted Child ego states. They try to get love by pleasing others, by knocking themselves out for strokes. Unfortunately, their Child ego states invariably pick the wrong people to try to please— the very people who just can't or won't give them the love they crave. Food becomes the substitute.

Typical hexes from the witch mother or the ogre father associated with this script are: "You're ugly," "You're not very pretty," "You're not good-looking," "You're not nice," "You're inconsiderate," "You're a disappointment to us," "You're dumb," and so forth. These hexes are not necessarily sent at the social level in the form of words. Very often they are sent at the psychological level, from a parent's Child to a child's Child. Ulterior messages conveyed by looks, glances, and facial expressions often say just as much as or more than words. In brief, the various hexes add up to one big hex: You're unlovable!

In response to the message "You're unlovable!" children often make a script decision. Here is the script decision made by Ruth A. when she was seven years old: "If I'm not lovable, I've got to try harder than the Number One people. Maybe nobody will notice that I'm ugly if I work hard, get good grades and am polite to grownups." Now an adult, Ruth works hard as a registered nurse, is an excellent cook, always remembers her parents' birthdays, treats her husband like the proverbial king, is alert to the needs of her children, and on the whole *plays second fiddle to the desires of other people.* She is also fat.

On the surface, "Looking for Love" may seem to be a winning script. Often there is much objective accomplishment in the person's life. The trouble is, the achievements are not for oneself; they are gifts given to one's parents, spouse, children, or friends in the hope of receiving strokes. But strokes received in this way are not very satisfying. Down deep there is the resentment that the stroke was not spontaneously given. And so the person with the "Looking for Love" script eats on and on, substituting food for love.

The common ending of a "Looking for Love" script is a

chronic depression from middle age on. After the age of forty, Ruth A. became increasingly alienated from her husband and children, and continued in a state of obesity. For years she had suffered from hypoglycemia, chronic low blood sugar. This condition developed into a case of diabetes—chronic high blood sugar. (Hypoglycemia is sometimes a forerunner of diabetes.) One way of looking at Ruth's behavior is to say that she is committing slow suicide. As a nurse, she knows how bad sugar is for her diabetic condition, yet continues to eat candies and desserts. The diabetes will probably be instrumental in bringing about her premature death. Death before the statistical life expectancy is frequently a part of self-destructive scripts.

The slow death of persons with a "Looking for Love" script is undramatic. Their lives undergo a long decline, just fizzling out. The poem "The Hollow Men" by T. S. Eliot concludes with the famous observation that the way the world ends is "Not with a bang but a whimper." This is the way the personal world of the individual with a Looking for Love fat-making script usually ends.

THE "CONQUEST OF FAT MOUNTAIN"

The "Conquest of Fat Mountain" is a variation on the basic "Looking for Love" script. Perhaps you have heard of the myth of Sisyphus. Sisyphus was doomed to push a heavy rock up a mountain. When he reached the pinnacle, the rock tumbled down to the bottom again. Poor Sisyphus had to repeat the task the next day—and the next—and the next—into eternity. I have known many fat Sisyphuses. One of them, Jennifer R., went from obese to normal weight and back to obese eight times in fifteen years. How can we explain a futile script like this?

Jennifer was a member of a women's weight-control group. She got a lot of praise and attention (strokes) as she was *losing* weight, but very little once the weight was lost. Her husband didn't stroke her for being a normal weight, and she felt in an emotional vacuum when she was away from the group. Her Child yearned for the applause she had received when she was giving the group spectacular weight losses of six and seven pounds a week. She had been a champion loser, receiving various pins and even a trophy for the greatest weight loss in a particular time period. The only way to be center stage again was to become obese, return to the group, and conquer Fat Mountain once more.

Although the majority of fat people do not follow this script quite as obviously as did Jennifer, the Yo-Yo syndrome is common. For many persons, alternately dieting and overeating has become a way of life. The Weight Problem plugs up the emptiness of life. It is a conversation piece, and it provides a way of getting strokes. ("You lost five pounds this week! That's just fantastic! How did you do it?") Overeaters who play the role of Sisyphus trap themselves in a stale behavior pattern that pointlessly repeats itself, contributing to the negative course of an underlying "Looking for Love" script.

"THE EVERYBODY LOOK AT ME" SCRIPT

The "Everybody Look at Me" script is lived out of the I'm OK —You're not OK life position. The roles played by persons with this script are similar: Fat Star, Fat Show-Off, Fat Manipulator, Fat Egomaniac, and Slob. The psychological structure of the person with an "Everybody Look at Me" script was detailed in Chapter Five, using Harry Q. as an example. You will recall that Harry has a large Permissive Parent and a big Rebellious Child. He has a tremendous need to express aggression, and one way he does it is by overeating. Persons like Harry really feel that they are entitled to devour the world, that "the world is their oyster."

Although a person with an Everybody Look at Me script may have been *told* the right thing to do by his parents, he was *programmed* to be a show-off and feel that it was OK to be this way. For example, three-year-old Linda is decorating the dining room walls with crayons. Linda's mother, Betty, catches her in the act and weakly protests, "Oh, no, dear. You shouldn't do that." This verbal statement is from her Parent. However, her posture and her expression indicate that Linda's activity is cute, and that Betty won't stop her. Betty's Child is saying at a psychological level to Linda's Child, "It's OK to draw on walls."

Linda, now six years old, has just taken her third helping of mashed potatoes and gravy. Betty says mildly, "That's too many potatoes, dear." Linda eats blissfully along, ignoring her mother. And Betty does nothing to stop Linda. Perhaps Betty has read somewhere that children should be given freedom when growing up, freedom to be themselves. True, but Betty is confusing freedom with license. When a child is given license, there are no reality-oriented limits imposed on his or her actions. And this is a serious mistake. In this case, the message from Betty's Child to Linda's Child is: "It's OK to eat three helpings of mashed potatoes and gravy at a single meal." This may not seem like a hex, but it is. It is a hex because it is destructive programming. It is an injunction that is not in the child's best interests, and will hurt the child over the years.

The person with an "Everybody Look at Me" script has often been given permission by the witch mother or the ogre father to be rude, inconsiderate, and self-centered. Such people may be described as undersocialized. Although they often manifest a superficial charm and stay out of trouble with the law, they are lawbreakers at heart. They "get away with murder" if they can.

The individual living life out of an "Everybody Look at Me" script will probably marry a Jellyfish Judy or a Cream-Puff Charlie—someone he or she can push around. Of course, Jellyfish Judy or Cream-Puff Charlie is quite likely to be following a "Looking for Love" script. The combination in a marriage of an "Everybody Look at Me" script with a "Looking for Love" script is a common one. One person feels that he or she is the star; the other feels like a moon that can be seen only in the reflected glory of the star. If both persons have been pro-grammed to overeat by childhood hexes, the script mixture only makes matters worse. The Jellyfish Judy or the Cream-Puff Charlie continues to follow the "Looking for Love" script, liter-ally looking for love in food—where it cannot be found.

And what is the culmination of the "Everybody Look at Me" script? How does life end for the Fat Star, the Fat Show-Off, the Fat Manipulator, the Fat Egomaniac, or the Slob? You will recall that the world usually ends not with a bang, but with a whimper for persons following Looking for Love scripts. The contrary is true for persons following Everybody Look at Me scripts. Their worlds often *do* end with a bang! They want to be noticed, to be looked at, to show off. Their deaths are often the last big hit of their lives. They are quite likely to die suddenly of an overdose, an unexpected accident, of alcoholism, a stroke, or a successful suicide attempt. By dying prematurely they sur-prise their families and friends. Fat stars don't want to end up as semi-invalids. They prefer to go out with a bang.

THE "GOING CRAZY" SCRIPT

The "Going Crazy" script is lived out of the I'm not OK—You're not OK position. The personality structure of persons with this kind of script was described in Chapter Five. Briefly, they may be characterized as confused and alienated. They tend to have a large Controlling Parent with contradictory mes-sages, a small Nurturing Parent, and very large Rebellious Child.

The witch mothers and the ogre fathers of the children who decided to adopt "Going Crazy" scripts hexed their children with mixed-up messages. The child received from the Child ego states of one or both of his parents messages such as: "You're fantastic; you're a great disappointment to us," or "You're beau-tiful; you're ugly," or "You're so intelligent; you're so stupid," or "You're creative; you have no originality," or "You eat too much; you don't eat enough," or "Go on a diet; go off a diet," or "You're too skinny; you're too fat." The self-image formed out of such double-bind messages is completely chaotic. The child grows up with no consistent sense of self.

In computer jargon there is the term GIGO. It stands for "Garbage In, Garbage Out." Let us say that you program a perfectly good computer with nonsense. Tell it that $2 + 2 = 5$. Now ask it, "What is $2 + 2$?" It answers 5. Garbage in, garbage out. The human nervous system is not too different. Program it with nonsense in the early years and it will produce nonsensical behavior in adult life. It does not require organic pathology for people to act crazy. A perfectly well-wired computer will give you nonsense if it has been fed nonsense. Similarly, many mental illnesses are not illnesses in any physiological, biological, or organic sense. They can be understood in terms of faulty programming, the parental injunctions as perceived by the Child ego state in the early years, years when the Adult was not sufficiently developed to help the Child discriminate between sense and nonsense.

Persons with a "Going Crazy" script usually search in late adolescence or early adulthood for a marriage partner who will help them go crazy. Their Child ego state has decided that they will go crazy, and they need someone to help them along. This someone will play the role of Persecutor to their Victim Going Crazy role. The Persecutor will be blamed by the Victim for his increasing sense of sadness, madness, confusion, and alienation. Almost always, persons who are "losing their minds" will say of their spouses, "He is driving me crazy," or "She is driving me crazy."

As you know, people who are diagnosed by psychiatrists as mentally ill do not usually receive such informal labels. Instead they are said to be suffering from "psychotic reactions," reactions in which contact with reality is more or less blurred. It is quite common to prescribe for psychotic patients various kinds of tranquilizing drugs. It seems clear to me that many people suffering from borderline or undiagnosed psychotic reactions (i.e., "Going Crazy" scripts) turn to food as a major tranquilizer. One of the actions of ingested food is to activate the parasympathetic division of the autonomic nervous system. When the sympathetic division is too active, the person is likely to be "hyper" or "manic," unable to concentrate, and prone to bizarre ideas. Eating offsets the hyperactivity and hyperemotionality. Many people with "Going Crazy" scripts overeat to soothe their jangled nerves, to find a bit of temporary calm in the midst of a psychological hurricane. They often find it necessary to seek the tranquilizing effect of food five or six times a day over and above their meals.

What is the upshot of the "Going Crazy" script—how does it usually end? It is difficult to generalize. Because it is a "Going Crazy" script it is literally "crazy"—meaning unpredictable. Some people with this script may sink down, down, down into a kind of slow psychological oblivion. They are said to be suffering from psychotic depression, a depression that goes deeply into their inner being. One patient called it "a black hole in psychological space." Brenda L., who plays the game of Fat Recluse described in Chapter Seven, provides us with one example of a person who is dying a slow death, who will probably go "with a whimper."

On the other hand, some persons with "Going Crazy" scripts decide to "go with a bang." Sometimes this is literal, as in the case of the individual who commits suicide with a gun. More commonly, the individual dies a "tragic" death—playing out the role of a Victim in a soap opera. Deaths associated with various kinds of accidents, strokes, and diseases arriving from "nowhere" all provide examples of melodramatic deaths.

For the person playing the role of Crazy Victim in a fat-making script, food is an analgesic, a tranquilizer, a balm to the troubled spirit. It provides a little warmth in a cold world.

THE COUNTERSCRIPT AND THE ANTISCRIPT

To complete our discussion of scripts, we must consider the TA concepts of the counterscript and the antiscript. Counterscripts and antiscripts are script variations that provide contrasting possibilities to the main script.

The counterscript represents parental precepts that were *told* to the child. As such, the counterscript comes from the Parent ego states of the parents (or other authority figures). The script, on the other hand, comes from the Child ego states of the parents, and represents what the child is *programmed* to do. The big difference between counterscript messages and script messages is that counterscript messages are "weak." They just sound good. They are the "right" thing to say, consisting of moralizing statements, advice, and lectures.

A typical fragment of a counterscript may go something like this: "I want you to grow up to be a beautiful, accomplished young woman. I want you to marry well, and live in a lovely home. I expect you to watch your figure and never be fat like me. When you see yourself gaining a few pounds, go on a diet right away and get it off promptly before it causes any trouble. Eat sweets very seldom—only on special occasions—and even then only in moderation." The witch mother or the ogre father might contradict this with a look or some other kind of psychological message that says, "Don't listen to all that goody-goody stuff. I want you to marry a fool or a slob, and get fat like me. I can't see why you should be happy if I'm not!" Thus the script is reinforced.

"Going on a diet" and "being good" are usually aspects of the counterscript, not the script. In such cases the "decision" to go on a diet is not a long-term decision to lose weight and keep it off; it is just a temporary pose arising from the counterscript. Behavior arising from the counterscript provides a temporary counterpoint to more entrenched behavior patterns arising from the script. Thus, almost always, the person who is following the counterscript will "go off the diet" and "stop being good." After flirting with the counterscript for a time—sometimes even for months and occasionally for years—the individual will return to the basic script.

Counterscript behavior can be distinguished from script behavior by the fact that it must be *willed,* there is *psychological effort* involved. When you are behaving out of your counterscript you feel that you are pulling a load uphill. For example, when you "go on a diet," you may feel at a deeper level that you are living for the day when you can "go off a diet." That is why the solution to one's weight problems hardly lies in the direction of the counterscript and "going on diets."

The antiscript is the opposite of the script. If the script says "up," the antiscript says "down." If the script says "eat," the antiscript says "don't eat." If the script says "be fat," the antiscript says "be skinny." Antiscript statements are mirror images, and as such are *totally* determined by script statements. For example, Grace R. had a "Looking for Love" script decided upon by her Adapted Child. In her early twenties, in a futile attempt to "undecide" her script, she let her Rebellious Child take over and direct a skinny-making antiscript. What this meant in practice is that she became phobic about food—she developed an irrational fear of it. The clinical label for such a condition is *anorexia nervosa,* a pathological abstinence from food found mainly in teen-age girls and young women. It is a tragic and useless way to try to break free from a fat-making script. In extreme cases, anorexia nervosa can lead to death if untended. Such patients have to be fed intravenous glucose.

Grace R. weighed about 145 pounds when she went into the antiscript. She lost weight rapidly, attaining a normal weight for her of about 115 pounds. She passed this weight, and eventually went down to eighty pounds. Although she has gained back about ten pounds, she still looks rather awful. She nibbles a bit, won't touch a sweet for love or money, and seems terrified by both food and possible obesity. She has made an uneasy truce with herself, and lives in constant fear that her fat-making "Looking for Love" script will once again rear its ugly head. She is obviously *not* free from her script. It is the basis, in mirror form, of every action of her antiscript.

BREAKING FREE FROM SCRIPTS

I am aware that reading about scripts can be somewhat discouraging. One has the feeling that one's destiny is determined, that the future is fixed. Nothing could be farther from the truth! The purpose of script analysis is not to make predictions, but to issue danger signals. The script analysis merely says, "If this trend continues, this is the way you are heading." But you are free to break the trend. If you see a warning signal at a railroad crossing, you do not say, "How depressing. I'm going to collide with a train." Instead you say, "I'll put on the brakes and stop." You *avoid* disaster. Similarly, knowing about scripts puts you in the position to avoid trouble. The script was a conscious decision made years ago by your Child. When you identify a self-destructive script and elevate it to consciousness, you have it in your power to unmake your inner Child's decision. Your thinking Adult has the ability to "undecide" the script and to place you on a more positive course in life.

If you feel that much of your behavior is determined by a script, here are some guidelines for breaking free:

1. Ask yourself what is your dominant life position. Is it I'm not OK—You're OK? Is it I'm OK—You're not OK? Is it I'm not OK—You're not OK? If it is one of these three down life positions, take note: each determines the choice of a fat-making self-destructive script. Decide from your Adult to adopt the only healthy life position, the I'm OK—You're OK life position.

2. In what ways were you hexed? In what ways were you cursed? Did your parents or other authority figures make

negative statements about your personality? Have these judgments become a part of your personality? What did your parents communicate from their Child ego states to your Child? What were their hang-ups and personal problems? Decide from your Adult that *you do not have to live by these hexes and curses today.* Understand that they were inflicted on you, that your Child identified with them, but that they are *not* you. If, for example, one of your parents predicted from a psychological level that you will never lose weight, vigorously reject this prediction. Realize that it was made out of your actual parent's emotional Child (the witch mother or the ogre father), and that it does not necessarily represent reality at all.

3. Identify your principal fat-making script. Is it the "Looking for Love" script? Is it the "Everybody Look at Me" script? Is it the "Going Crazy" script? Although these scripts overlap and interact, the principal script usually stands out as a dominant theme. Once you have determined which of the three principal fat-making scripts most closely approximates your situation in life, decide from your Adult that the script *is not for you.* Visualize it as a strait jacket, something that confines you. And you are going to wriggle free.

4. Be aware that in the long run scripts are self-defeating and self-destructive. Although a script may bring a certain amount of short-run satisfaction, in the long run it may have undesirable, and sometimes tragic, consequences. From your Adult, think: "I will place my chips with constructive long-run behavior, *not* with destructive short-run behavior. I will place my overall welfare over the psychological satisfactions of the moment."

5. Understand that your script was not chosen by your thoughtful Adult, but by your Child. Ask yourself if you want to live your life on the basis of childish decisions. Assert from your Adult, *"I* will decide how to live my life, not my inner Child of the past."

6. Do not be deceived into thinking that behavior deter-

mined by a counterscript or an antiscript represents script-free living. These behaviors represent attempts to break free from the script, but they are totally enmeshed in the script. When you are doing what you were told to do (counterscript), you are certainly not free. And when you are rebelling against the script by doing the opposite of what it programs you to do (antiscript), you are also certainly not free. From your Adult say to yourself, "The road to personal freedom does not reside in doing either what I was told to do or by rebelling childishly against the script. I must think through what is the rational thing to do with my life and my eating behavior. I recognize that most reducing diets drawn up by others represent versions of the counterscript. They are 'nice' things I'm told to do. And that is one reason I eventually go off them. I also recognize that starving myself, crash dieting, or becoming phobic about food all represent versions of the antiscript. In order to lose weight and keep it off I must follow a rational middle course of action determined by my Adult."

7. Be clear on the fact that the rewards of script-free living are great: freedom from fat, autonomy as a person, and intimacy with others. Using your Adult, consciously think: "I *can* be free from fat. I *can* live my own life and control its outcomes. I *can* have emotional closeness with the people I care about."

8. Decide *now* that scripts can be "undecided," that you *can* break free! Start living from your thinking Adult, not your emotional Child.

In the words of Britain's great nineteenth-century prime minister Benjamin Disraeli, "We make our fortunes and we call them fate." Implicit in Disraeli's remark is the TA assertion that you can break free of a self-determined fate, and consciously turn in the direction of productive self-directed living, a kind of living that, if you are fat, will carry you toward a normal weight.

9

Using Your Adult to Lose Weight

The phrase *using your Adult* is synonymous with such familiar expressions as: "Use your head," "Think for yourself," and "Wake up." All these expressions imply the capacity for conscious action, rational thought, and realistic decision. A basic assumption of TA is that you have a thinking self—your Adult —and that this thinking self can be activated to serve your best long-run interests. In this book, your best long-range interests refer to ways you can use your Adult to help you lose weight successfully and keep it off.

The Parent and the Child are the parts of the personality that belong to the past. The Parent represents the past in terms of prejudices and biases, the things you were taught are right and wrong about the world. The Child represents the past in terms of feelings, all the emotions you experienced while you were growing up. Whenever your Parent button or your Child button is pushed, an old "tape" is activated. This tape tells you what to think or how to feel, and *it may be inappropriate for the present.* In contrast, the Adult is oriented to reality and represents the *present* and the *future.* Only by being fully aware via your Adult of the future consequences of present actions can you be really in charge of your life.

Throughout this book I have shown you ways your Adult can help you lose weight. I have provided explicit guidelines for actively using your Adult to break free from old Parent or Child tapes, to counteract the effects of advertising on your Child, to change fat-making transactions into Adult-Adult transactions, to end games fat people play, and to break free from fat-making scripts. We have come a long way. In this chapter I offer additional ways your Adult can help you lose weight.

INSIGHT AND ACTION

Insight and action are both related to ways you can use your Adult to lose weight. *Insight* is "seeing into" the nature of a problem. Applied to weight control, it means developing self-understanding about why you eat. Much of this book has been concerned with why people overeat. At this point you should have some fairly adequate answers to this question. However, the *why* of the matter is not enough. Understanding why you overeat without knowing *how* you can do something about it can be compared to the situation of a ship at sea with radar but with no steering mechanism. Its radar penetrates the fog and tells it that there is an iceberg up ahead. But the ship is unable to respond to the message. This was a central flaw of classical Freudian psychoanalysis. It supposed that insight was enough to bring about behavioral change. But it is not. Self-understanding may be necessary for change, but it is not sufficient. When the knowledge of *how to do* something is combined with insight—the *why* of the situation—then rapid and constructive behavioral change is possible. This is where the concept of action comes in.

Action in the present context refers to intelligent action determined by your Adult. It means actually doing something about your weight problem rather than just reading about it, talking about it, thinking about it, and trying to understand it. I have stressed the importance of action in other chapters, and in this chapter the theme will be a dominant one. It is the call to action that is the central point of behavior therapy and its applications to weight control. Behavior modification strategies are designed to help one break habits and conditioned responses (old Parent and Child tapes). They are derived from a large body of traditional psychological knowledge known as *learning theory,* which is associated with such great figures in psychology as Ivan Pavlov, John B. Watson, and B. F. Skinner.

Unfortunately, sometimes psychoanalysis and behavior therapy are presented in either-or terms. One is in either the psychoanalytic camp or the behavior therapy camp. One must take sides. Perhaps this is necessary in hammering out theories and in the development of a field of study. However, it's simply pointless if you have an overeating problem and you're looking for all the help you can get. You want answers to both your *why* questions and your *how* questions. As I see it, this is the great strength of TA, and the reason I have written this entire book around TA as applied to weight control. TA gives us insight. It reveals why people overeat. TA also gives us ideas for taking action. Through its formulation of the thinking Adult, we see ways we can break old patterns and move toward new ones. The Adult is at once the personality's agent of understanding and the personality's agent for action. TA is thus able to combine in one approach the concepts of insight and action.

WAYS OF GETTING STROKES

As you well know, one of the principal reasons people overeat is a chronic stroke hunger. What can be done to diminish this nagging stroke hunger in nonfattening ways? Here are some suggestions:

1. *Give good strokes yourself.* Be warm and loving toward others. Compliment your spouse or boyfriend or girlfriend whenever possible, give proper attention to the accom-

plishments of your children, and display respect for your friends. Don't make the people you care about have to work too hard to earn strokes from you. Give unconditional strokes. I know. You may feel that your unconditional positive strokes are taken for granted, that your spouse or boyfriend or girlfriend and others know how to receive but not how to give. But keep in mind that you'll never get strokes if you don't give them. If you really are in the presence of people who are unable to return love, there are other possibilities we can explore.

2. *Ask for strokes.* There are two ways to ask for strokes, directly and indirectly. Infants and preschoolers ask for strokes directly, without guile. A baby who wants attention cries for it until a parent picks him up. A preschooler says artlessly, "Look at me, Mommy!" or "Watch this, Daddy!" Adults, too, in our society can ask for a stroke directly when in the presence of someone they love and trust. Between lovers, husband and wife, or parent and child it is quite natural to say such things as: "Hold my hand," or "Rub my back," or "Give me a hug before I go," or "I could sure use a massage," or "How about a kiss?" or "Squeeze me," or "Sit by me for a while."

In less intimate relationships, we use our social skills to ask for strokes indirectly, thus protecting ourselves against possible rebuffs. Thus we will say to a co-worker, "Are you free for lunch?" which may translate at the psychological level into: "I like you. Do you like me?" If the co-worker says, "Sure, I'm free. Where would you like to go?" we feel stroked. We have been recognized in a positive way. It's as if the person has said, "I like you too."

Unfortunately, there are persons who are so shy and inhibited that they will not even ask for strokes indirectly. Although they suffer from a substantial stroke hunger, they wait for someone else to make the first move. Sometimes this never happens. (Maybe the other person is shy too!) Persons who are excessively shy need to learn how to take small risks to obtain strokes. The old saw "Nothing ventured, nothing gained" is appropriate here. *Shyness: What It Is, What to Do About It,* by psychologist Philip G. Zimbardo, contains practical suggestions for shy persons.

My clients sometimes protest, "I ask for strokes, and I don't get them!" If you also have such a complaint, I would guess that you are looking for strokes from the wrong people. Pick your sources. Ask for strokes from loving persons, not from persons who want to play manipulative games. If you insist that there are no loving persons in your private world, I suggest that you start looking for them. The world is full of nice people. They exist. Really they do.

3. *Stroke yourself.* It isn't hard to stroke yourself. All you have to do is say from your Nurturing Parent to your Child, "You're OK," or "I like you," or "You really look great in that outfit," or "You did a good job on that," or something similar. Unfortunately, many people have gotten in the habit of putting themselves down. Instead of stroking themselves, they give their Child discounts from their Critical Parent. They say things like: "You're not OK," or "I don't like you," or "You look hideous in that outfit," or "Here's a flaw in your work." These discounts only add to their chronic stroke hunger. From your thinking Adult, decide now that these self-destructive patterns are not for you, that you *are* OK, and that you will deliberately stroke yourself.

4. *Seek stroking situations.* Look for a class, a club, a job, volunteer work, group activities, or other social settings in which you can get your fair share of attention and recognition. Don't just sit around feeling sorry for yourself. Do something to alter your life style if it is not providing you with emotional satisfaction.

5. *Accept strokes graciously.* If someone gives you a positive stroke, let the other person know you are pleased. When we pet a cat, it purrs. And the person petting the cat enjoys the cat's purr. Similarly, we should respond to positive strokes with appropriate recognition of the other in-

dividual's gift to us. Let's say that a friend sincerely praises you for a job well done. Don't say, "Oh, it was nothing." False modesty is no more becoming than a tendency to brag. Your friend will not feel like complimenting you a second time. The best way to respond to sincere praise is by looking directly into the other person's eyes and saying with equal sincerity, "Thank you!" You may even add in some cases, "That really makes me feel good." This is like the cat's purr, and it will not turn the person off. On the contrary, it is very rewarding to the other person, and he will be encouraged to give you more strokes in the future.

ASSERTIVE LIVING AND ASSERTIVE EATING

The advice I have just given you—to seek stroking situations—ties in with an important concept that has come into prominence of late. It is the concept of *assertiveness*. Assertiveness is a middle way between passivity and aggression. It is my observation that most overeaters err in the direction of passivity. They're in the I'm not OK—You're OK life position. Thus they allow themselves to be oppressed, ordered about, and put down. They take discounts standing still, which not only increases their general feeling of being unloved, but also makes them deeply angry. The Controlling Parent tells them to hold back their anger. And this gives us the following formula: Anger + Repression = Depression. Chronic depression is in turn associated with overeating. One way out of this bind is to seek ways of becoming more assertive.

The key to behaving assertively is to behave out of your Adult. For example, when someone criticizes you unfairly, you don't have to agree passively (Child) or act counteraggressively (Parent). You can get into your Adult and say directly and firmly to the other person's Adult, "I don't see it that way." You are asserting yourself without putting the other person down.

Here are four important assertive skills:

1. *Begin your sentences with I.* When you say, "I'm angry," or "I don't see it that way," or "I don't want any pie," you are sending a message about your inner condition. As such, it can hardly be disputed by the other party. The other individual is really a fool if he says, "Yes, you want the pie." However, if you begin your retorts with *you,* there is a great potential for trouble. "You're being unfair," or "You're wrong," or "You're trying to pressure me to eat," are fighting words, and should be avoided.

2. *Engage in more feeling talk.* Get your feelings out in the open. Say things like: "I'm depressed" or "I hated that movie" more often. Don't wait to see the way the wind blows among your companions. You have a mind and feelings. Express yourself. It's your right to do so. Feeling talk is a good antidote against the depression that so many overweight people feel. Don't be a psychological marshmallow. It leads to being a physical marshmallow.

3. *Use the "broken record" technique.* This technique is just what it sounds like. You stand your ground and repeat your position. For example, you are asked by a hostess to take a piece of pie and you don't want any. You say, "I don't want any pie, thank you." The hostess says, "But I made it just for you." You say, "I'm sorry, but I don't want any pie." (Keep smiling!) "But why don't you want any pie?" asks the hostess. You say, "I just don't want any." (You might be kind enough to say, "I'm not hungry." This is an existential message. But *don't* say, "I'm on a diet," or you may be in for a sales pitch about "Just this once . . .")

4. *Try fogging.* When you are dealing with a manipulative person who is trying in various ways to get you to eat or drink against your best interests, you can fog. This means to agree in principle, but to promise nothing. For example, "You're right. I really should have a piece of Billy's birthday cake. But I'm just so full that I can't eat a bite. Will you wrap up a piece for me so I can take it home?" Notice you haven't promised to actually eat it, only to

take it home. When you get it home, you can put it in the freezer, give it to the neighbors, feed it to the dog, or throw it in the garbage can. ("Oh, horrors!" cries your Controlling Parent. "Mustn't waste food!" Turn back to Chapter Two and review the analysis of what it really means to waste food.)

Assertive eating is a natural consequence of assertive living. Not only do you have the right to say no when another person tries to stuff extra food into you; you also have the right to say no to the food itself. When a tempting food item speaks to you: "Eat me, eat me! I'm good!" you have the right to say, "Not now. Maybe some other time. The answer is *no!*" From your Adult, say to yourself: "Food is not my master. I am not its slave. I do not have to obey when it commands that I eat."

Assertive eating also implies the right to say yes to food. Ask yourself what you really want to eat, what will really satisfy your Child, and be sure to eat those foods on occasion. For example, I allow myself a dessert *of my own choosing* two or three times a month. A real treat—like a hot fudge sundae. But *I* seek it out, *I* make the choice of where and when to eat it. It is not pushed on me. Thus when I'm at a wedding and I'm offered white cake—which my Child craves not at all—I can easily refuse it. A person who does not practice assertive eating will passively accept the white cake with the rationalization: "I've been dieting and I haven't had a treat for a week," and still be dissatisfied. Such persons are "sitting ducks" for *any* temptation that comes along. They feel so deprived that they are unable to assert themselves against food. I cannot overstress the point. Assertive eating includes the right to say yes to food when you make a responsible decision out of your Adult, a decision that takes your long-range interests into account. Assertive eating also includes the right to say no to food that you know you should not have. Neither the food itself nor another person has the authority to com-

mand you to eat. When you accept false authority, you
behave out of your Child. When you operate from your
own authority, you behave out of your Adult.

UNMAKING FAT-MAKING HABITS

Much overeating is determined by habits. Habits are predictable behavioral routines. The most obvious example is this one:
See food→ eat food. In other words, a stimulus (food) leads to
a predictable response (eating). This is the essence of a habit: a
stimulus triggers a particular response. In other words, a habit
is a programmed routine, an *unthinking* behavioral sequence.
As such, habits arise from your Parent and your Child. Behavior
decided upon by your Adult cannot by definition be a habit.
Thus the key to unmaking and/or modifying bad habits is to get
your Adult into the act and *jam* the programs coming out of
your Parent and/or Child.

In Chapter Four I introduced the concept of stimulus-
induced eating. You may remember that such eating is induced
not only by food, but by *food-related cues.* Food-related cues
can—unfortunately—include *anything* that has come to be associated with food. Examples are food signs, menus, other people eating, smells, pictures, word descriptions of food, the sight
of the refrigerator, or a time of day when you regularly eat.
These are all external cues—sources outside you. However,
food-related cues can also include internal states such as feelings of depression, anger, anxiety, restlessness, tension, or boredom. These internal states, called *covert cues,* may be the trig-
ger that sends you on a search for food. In the context of TA,
let us think of them as demands arising from your Child. Obviously, the way to unmake your fat-making habits is to break the
link between the cue—external or internal—and the programmed behavior. A number of ideas have been offered in
previous chapters. To use them to your own advantage, conduct
what I call a *habitanalysis.*

In order to make an actual habitanalysis (as opposed to thinking about it or talking about it or reading about it), it is necessary that you acquire a set of index cards. On the front of a card specify *one* of your bad eating habits. For example, "When I'm home alone and I'm bored I start looking in the refrigerator." Note that you haven't tried to list all your bad eating habits on one card. It is very important to realize that your overeating habit is *not* one Big Bad Habit, but a *set* of bad eating habits. Use as many index cards as habits you are able to identify. As others occur to you, list them. Within a few days you should have a fairly complete collection—one to a card—of your bad eating habits.

Now go through this book and jot down on the back of the card ideas that suggest themselves to you from your reflective Adult for ways that you can unmake, modify, or manage the undesirable eating habit. Keep in mind that it is important to specify on each card the external or internal cue that triggers unnecessary eating. If you really get into this and brainstorm it, your Adult will begin to produce a host of ways you can jam old habit programs. For example, on the back of a card in which boredom was cited as the internal cue for overeating, one of my clients wrote: "I love to do needlepoint and I've gotten away from it. I'm going to always have a needlepoint project out and ready to work on. When I get bored, I'll go straight to the needlepoint and get involved with it for a while. The time will be spent constructively, and I can't use my hands to stuff my face when they're busy with needle and thread." Of course, her suggestion will not necessarily work for you. Put your Adult to work to find ways of coping with bad eating habits that are tailored to your unique personality.

Collect all the cards and work on only one or two at a time. I recommend selecting the easiest ones first—the ones that promise the greatest likelihood of success. Each actual success creates greater confidence, and momentum tends to build as you move forward through the habits. A habitanalysis is an organized, systematic, and *direct* way of approaching your eating problems. As such, I encourage you to use it.

FREEDOM FROM EMOTIONAL SLAVERY

As we have seen, much excessive eating is induced by negative emotional states. The three principal culprits in this regard seem to be anger, depression, and anxiety. Indeed, these emotions are closely related. Much chronic depression is associated with repressed anger. Anger, in turn, is often repressed out of anxiety, anxiety about being rejected by another person if anger is expressed. Say that a married woman, Carol, is in the I'm not OK—You're OK position. Her husband has just done something very frustrating. What is her first impulse? Probably to say, "I'm angry with you. How could you do such a thing?" But if she is anxiety-ridden about her ability to hold on to her husband, if she is fearful of rejection, she may let the incident pass without comment. If this is done too often, her Child will begin to feel used and abused. Storing up anger will lead to depression. That is why assertive living is important. Speaking one's mind and practicing the assertive skill called feeling talk will help one avoid the build-up of anger that often underlies depression.

I should like to issue a caution here: not all emotions are legitimate. In some cases we can speak of unwarranted anger, and unwarranted depression. Where do these unwarranted emotions come from? They come from the simplistic either-or thinking of the Child. Let's say that Arlene's husband comes home from work one hour late without calling her. Going into her Child, she thinks: "He doesn't love me. If he loved me he'd be considerate enough to call!" Now, Arlene's husband was certainly wrong not to call. But it is a gross overgeneralization to make the judgment: "He doesn't love me!" out of his transgression. However, Arlene's fantasy-oriented Child expects her husband to be Prince Charming. And certainly Prince Charming wouldn't keep Cinderella waiting without explanation for an hour. Maybe yesterday Arlene's husband took her out to dinner. Maybe last month he bought her something she really wanted for her birthday. But her Child does not see past the moment.

Let's say that while Arlene is waiting for her tardy husband and simultaneously feeling unloved, she copes by stroking herself with food. How can she counteract this pattern and her negative emotions? One strategy she can use is to challenge her own thinking processes. From her Adult she can ask herself reality-oriented questions. "Does it really mean that he doesn't love me because he wasn't considerate enough to call this time? Is it rational to expect that anyone will be constantly considerate, thoughtful, and sensitive?" Pondering these questions, she will realize that her emotions are being determined by her Child. As such, they are illegitimate emotions, emotions out of proportion to the offense. Seeing the situation from the Adult transforms the emotional reaction from a storm into a transient cloudburst. Of course, Arlene will still be annoyed with her husband—and properly so. And when he comes home she should say, "I was so annoyed. I expected you to call!" (I-messages.) This allows Arlene to express her feeling. It also allows her husband to give a rational response from his Adult. He can see that she is irritated, but he doesn't feel put down. The important thing to note here is that by using her Adult, Arlene can keep her emotions from escalating.

The situation described with Arlene has a basic psychological structure typical of many situations that produce adverse emotional reactions. First, there is a frustrating event. Second, there is the Child's input: "This is terrible," or "I'm a failure," or "It's a catastrophe," or "They don't love me," or "I'm no good," or "I'll never live this down." Third, there is the illegitimate emotional reaction, an emotion that is excessive and inappropriate to the actual situation. Fourth, there is the unnecessary eating induced by the emotion.

The way to jam this particular program is at the level of the Child's input. Make a conscious decision to get into your Adult and challenge the Child's thinking. Ask yourself, "Is this really terrible? Or is it merely disappointing?" "Is this a catastrophe? Or is it just a letdown?" "Is it really true that they don't love me? Or am I overreacting because of my not OK feelings?" "Is it rational to think that I'll *never* live this down? Or will it all be forgotten in about a week?" It is my conviction that persons can learn to use the Adult to jam either-or thought patterns arising from the Child. It is a matter of becoming aware of these thought patterns and recognizing that the emotions they produce are excessive. Learning to be free from emotional slavery is one of the most effective ways your Adult can help you lose weight. By reducing the impact of illegitimate emotions, you can greatly reduce the likelihood that they will induce you to eat.

PSYCHOLOGICAL DISTANCE AND FIELD INDEPENDENCE

One of the reasons stimulus-induced eating is so common among overweight persons is that they seem to be hypersensitive to food-related cues. They are much more aware than the normal eater that over there is a sign proclaiming the presence of a coffee shop, that it's only five minutes until lunchtime, that pretty soon the cake is going to be served at the birthday party, that the Smiths usually serve hors d'oeuvres before dinner, that there is a delightful smell coming from the oven, and that someone at the next table is eating a delicious-looking dessert. In other words, food and anything associated with it create a *psychological field* for the overeater, a field not unlike a magnetic field. And the hapless overeater is like an iron filing in the magnetic field. He passively obeys the dictates of the field. If the field says, "Come over here. Enter this coffee shop," he goes. If the field says, "Stuff yourself with snacks before dinner," he does so. If the field says, "Look at those people enjoying that dessert at the next table. Don't you see what you're missing?" he is prone to order a dessert too.

What the chronic overeater clearly needs is *independence* from the field. But how? Let us answer the question by asking another question: Why is he captured by the field in the first place? He is captured because various elements of the field activate certain Child tapes. When these tapes start to play, they dictate behavior. Behavior dictated by the Child tapes is *unthinking*. The way to achieve independence from the field is to enter the Adult and use it to keep the old tapes from playing. A number of ways of doing this have already been discussed. In the context of the present discussion, one way of doing this is to create what I call *psychological distance*.

The concept of psychological distance can be understood in relation to the more familiar concept of physical distance. Say that you are visiting friends and a bowl of peanuts is placed on the table near you. You find yourself behaving out of your Child, eating more peanuts than you ought to. At last you say, "Please put these peanuts at the other end of the table, where I can't reach them." When they are at the other end of the table, you are much less likely to be controlled by them. Why? Because when they are a few inches away you are in the position of a child in a candy store, right in front of the display cabinets. It's pretty hard for the child to resist the candy. When you place the peanuts at the other end of the table you are in the position of a child *outside* the candy store. There is at least the *possibility* of thought, reflection, and analysis. You must consciously *decide* to ask for the peanuts or go get them. Whenever you are in a position where you must make a decision, you activate your Adult. And your Adult just might make an intelligent decision in favor of your long-range best interests.

However, it is not always possible to place physical distance between yourself and food. In many situations the food is just there, and you remain close to it: while attending a party in which hors d'oeuvres are being served before dinner, sitting at a holiday table loaded with food, facing a large plate of food in a restaurant, being present at a birthday party when cake and ice cream is being served, and so forth. Nevertheless, it *is* possible to create psychological distance in such situations by operating from your Adult. Here are some specific ways:

1. From your Adult say to yourself, "This food is pressing my Child button. But I don't have to obey my Child. I'm grown up, and I have the power of decision. In this case I'm going to use the power of decision to say no to the food."

2. Use an exercise I call *x-raying the food.* You have heard, of course, of Superman and his x-ray vision. Well, imagine that you have x-ray vision. In your mind's eye look *into* the food and break it into its elements. For example, let's say that you are trying to place psychological distance between yourself and a piece of pie. You x-ray the pie, and you "see" that it is made out of hydrogenated fat, refined sugar, and white flour. You say to yourself from your Adult, "I really don't need that hydrogenated fat to raise my cholesterol level, the refined sugar to raise my triglyceride level, and the fat-making calories in the white flour. I see the pie at this moment not as a tempting treat, but as an agent of my destruction."

3. Learn all you can about nutrition and proper eating. Information gathered by your Adult will change the perception of your Child. When you are in the presence of food, invoke your knowledge of some of the hazards of overeating and the presence of food additives to reduce the desirability of indiscriminately ingesting food. You might ask yourself, depending on the food item, "Do I really need more tricalcium phosphate or sodium nitrate or monosodium glutamate or benzoyl peroxide or butylated hydroxyanisole or butylated hydroxytoluene in my system?" (I do not mean to suggest that all these additives will be found in one food item. But learn to read the fine print on labels. You will be surprised.) If you are trying to resist something served with white bread, such as a hamburger, you might memorize this description offered by author Max Shulman in his humorous novel *Anyone Got a Match?* about the

tobacco and food industries: "In order to make white bread white—I speak now of common commercial-grade white bread, not of French, Italian, or other crusty breads—the flour must first be chemically emulsified, oxidized, hydrogenated, neutralized, stabilized, and, most significant, bleached with chlorine dioxide." This kind of mental recital may very well create psychological distance between you and the bread.

Does this mean you should never eat white bread again and avoid all foods with additives? No, of course not. I'm not saying that at all. I eat white bread from time to time. (But I *do* prefer to eat whole-grain bread whenever possible.) I eat all sorts of foods with preservatives and additives. It is pretty hard to function in our society without doing so. But I *am* saying it is good to be aware of these things, and I am particularly emphasizing the way you can use this awareness to create psychological distance between you and the food.

4. Memorize the poem "Invictus." It appears in Chapter Five. When you are in the presence of food, consciously and deliberately recite the poem to yourself. Give particular emphasis to the last two lines: "I am the master of my fate: I am the captain of my soul." Reflect on what these words mean, and you will find yourself much less spellbound by food.

5. Learn to release your eating utensils several times during a meal. Yes, actually *put down* the fork. Let it go. And mentally count slowly to ten or twenty before picking it up again. Most overeaters keep a death grip on the fork throughout the meal, setting it down only to reach for a beverage. While your fork is released, just sit quietly for a moment and think about something you have learned from TA about overeating. (No, it won't look odd. Most of the people you eat with are too busy eating themselves to pay much attention to your behavior. If they do notice, what you are doing is not *that* odd. You're just taking a ten-

second break from eating.) There is nothing as effective as a delay to activate the Adult.

6. Another thing you can do during a meal is get up and take a brief walk. For example, go to the sink and get a glass of water. While you are at the sink, look at your empty place at the table and imagine yourself sitting there. Ask yourself if you would be able to pass up a second helping of a particular item. Or reflect on your reasons for wanting to lose weight (for example, health or appearance). Or recite the poem "Invictus" mentally. Or say to yourself from your Adult, "I'm under no real compulsion to overeat. It's a decision I make. Every time I make an eating mistake I'm deciding against myself, against my best long-range interests. Am I for myself or against myself?" Actually, anything you think about that is reality-oriented and focuses on your welfare will help you to increase the psychological distance between you and food.

7. Say that you are alone in your residence, and you have an urge to engage in some unnecessary snacking. Another delaying tactic that can be used to activate your Adult and increase psychological distance is to set a three-minute egg timer before eating. Say to yourself that you will wait at least three minutes before going to the refrigerator. During the three minutes plug into your Adult and ask yourself if you have any options or alternatives to eating. Is there some conflicting activity you can pursue? Is there something nonfattening you can eat? In other words, during the delay, take the opportunity to use your Adult and think about what you are doing. This will help you to jam the Child program and also to gain greater independence from the psychological field created by food and food-related cues.

CONCENTRATION ON EATING

As you are well aware, a great deal of eating is done subconsciously. For example, you are out to dinner with friends, chatting happily, and to your dismay you look down and see an almost empty plate. Somebody else has been eating your food! No, it's not Goldilocks. But it is another child—your inner Child. Yes, your Child has eaten the food and *you* haven't really had a chance to enjoy it. This kind of experience is doubly negative when the food your Child has eaten is something you can ill afford in terms of calories and/or carbohydrates. Actually, if you become more aware of the act of eating itself, you will (1) enjoy your food more—actually taste it—and (2) reduce the invitational characteristics of food.

The psychological exercise described below is to be practiced only for a bite or two during a meal. If you ate this way all the time, it would take you forever to eat. The method used in this exercise can be called *sensory focusing,* because it requires you to focus on the physical sensations involved in eating. Here is the exercise:

1. Look at the food item for one minute. Try to "take it all in" with your eyes. Practice the exercise given earlier called x-ray, in which you psychologically break the food down into its elements. For example, if you are looking at a piece of pie, try to visualize the starch, sugar, hydrogenated fat, and chemical additives of which it is composed.
2. Consciously take a moderate-sized bite of the food. If it is a finger food such as a sandwich or French fries, do this cleanly with your front teeth, using a cutting, not a ripping or tearing action.
3. Now hold the food in your mouth for one minute without chewing. Just let it rest in your mouth, stimulating the sensory nerve endings on your tongue.

4. Now chew slowly as if in a slow-motion movie. While doing this concentrate on the food's texture. Is it smooth, grainy, granulated, crunchy, etc.?
5. Concentrate on the taste of the food. Is it primarily sweet, sour, bitter, or salty?
6. Continue chewing slowly until the food is completely liquefied, until it has no solid substance at all. Do not swallow until this point is reached.
7. Swallow. Make sure your mouth is completely clear of food before taking another bite.

As I said before, it is impractical to eat all your food this way. But you can modify the exercise to suit your own personality. Practicing any portion of it from time to time helps to free you from stimulus-induced eating.

WRITING DIALOGUES BETWEEN EGO STATES

Another way of activating your Adult is to write out dialogues between your ego states. This will help you to objectify the ego states, and in particular help you to decontaminate your Adult. (You will recall that in TA theory, contamination of the Adult takes place when the Parent and/or Child encroaches upon the Adult's psychological territory.) You hold dialogues between ego states in your head anyway, but these are often subliminal and circular. Placing a dialogue *in writing* can help you break free from self-defeating patterns.

Here is a typical dialogue submitted by one client, Loretta U.:

ADULT: OK, what's the problem? Parent, you go first.
PARENT: This silly person has no self-control. She eats eight or ten times a day. She's a slob.
ADULT: That's pretty general. Let's pick just one thing she's doing wrong—a real problem we can work on.
PARENT: OK. Every night around eleven she starts to pick on

peanuts. More often than not she eats half a jar. I think she should cut it out entirely. Just break the stupid habit. It's only a form of childish self-indulgence. Why can't she use her will power and take hold of herself the way other people do?

ADULT: Child, it's your turn. What's your reaction to this?

CHILD: I want the peanuts, I want the peanuts, I want the peanuts! I don't care what the Parent says. I want the peanuts! I'm not getting that much fun out of life! Why take away my little pleasures?

PARENT: *Little* pleasure? You call eating half a jar of peanuts at one time a little pleasure?

ADULT: OK, OK—I get the picture. Look, you two, we really have to work out some sort of practical compromise. Both of you have your own demands, and they're in conflict. See what you think of this idea. Let's modify the habit instead of breaking it completely. I'll count out exactly seven nuts and place them in a bowl. Then we'll expect Loretta to sit down and eat them *consciously,* practicing the sensory focusing exercise in which you concentrate on eating. I think she can make the nuts last as long as ten or fifteen minutes this way. She can extract a lot of pleasure out of a few nuts. This way, Parent, you should be satisfied—seven nuts can't do much damage. And this way, Child, you should be satisfied too—you'll have your oral pleasure. What do you think?

PARENT: It's worth a try.

CHILD: OK, I'm willing to try it too.

I might add that Loretta U. found that her Adult's middle-of-the-road approach works for her. She discovered an effective way to manage a long-standing eating problem.

THE SKILLFUL WILL

Overeaters talk a lot about will power. You will often hear them say, "If only I had some will power, I could lose weight." What they are talking about is the Victorian concept of will power, or the *iron will* which is used to repress or block desire and temptation. Obviously, this kind of will power usually fails. It comes out of the Parent, and in time it is usually overwhelmed by the stronger emotional pressures coming from the Child. So let's discard the concept of the iron will. It won't help you lose weight.

However, if we look upon the human will more as a steering mechanism than as a brake, we are likely to get somewhere. I thus introduce here psychiatrist Roberto Assagioli's concept of the *skillful will,* a will in which one uses the Adult to make intelligent decisions and realistic choices, a will based on insight and sensible action. In *The Act of Will* Assagioli has this to say about the skillful will:

> The skillful aspect of the will consists of the ability to obtain desired results with the least possible expenditure of energy. In order to go somewhere, one does not proceed by walking in a straight line across open country or by climbing over buildings. One rather studies a road map and uses existing roads, which, although not in a straight line, can lead one to his destination with the least amount of effort. And one takes advantage of already existing means of transportation, that is, of vehicles that are going in the direction he has chosen.
>
> Similarly, in order to use our will most skillfully, we need to understand our inner constitution, become acquainted with our many different functions, drives, desires, habit patterns, and the relationships between them, so that at any one time we can activate and utilize those aspects of ourselves that already have the tendency to produce the specific action or condition we are aiming for.*

*Roberto Assagioli, *The Act of Will* (New York: Viking Press, 1973), pp. 15–16.

I am in total accord with this passage from Assagioli's book. The techniques we have discussed in this chapter such as assertive eating, habitanalysis, and ways of increasing the psychological distance between yourself and food all involve the skillful will. Sometimes I call these techniques *management strategies,* emphasizing the idea that even if we cannot completely eliminate the tendency to make eating errors, we can modify and manage the tendency. But what you call this approach doesn't make much difference. The basic idea is that success in weight control resides in learning to work *with* yourself, not against yourself.

AN ADULT EATING PLAN

As you know by now, I am against "going on a diet" in the usual sense. The phrase "going on a diet" is a Parent phrase. It suggests to too many people a psychological strait jacket. Let's replace the concept of diet with the concept of an *Adult eating plan,* a flexible plan you can live with for life. An Adult eating plan does not contain rigid rules, but realistic guidelines. What might be an Adult eating plan for one person will not be a practical plan for another person. So I can't draw up *the* Adult eating plan and print it here. *Your* Adult has to draw up the eating plan that will work for you. The plan should be based on all that you know about nutrition and weight control. I can, however, offer an example of an Adult eating plan drawn up by one of my clients, Diane O. You can use it as a starting point for drawing up your own Adult eating plan. Here is Diane's plan:

1. *Calories.* I *hate* to count calories (my Child speaking!). But I know that in terms of my height (5'1"), I need about 2,500 a day. So I'm going to have this as a rough background figure. I'm going to try to stay within 2,000 to 3,000 a day as a basic guideline. But I'm not going to write it all down. I know the calorie counts of most foods, and I know when I'm going over, when I'm eating too much for me.

2. *Carbohydrates*. According to the carbohydrate gram books, I should keep my carbohydrate grams to about thirty or forty a day. Actually, I think there's something to this. It seems to me that when I get too much sugar or starch it tends to go to fat. Anyway, I'm going to watch my carbohydrates and most days keep them within thirty or forty grams.

3. *Vitamins and minerals*. I'm going to eat right—not too many junk foods, and plenty of fresh fruits and vegetables. So I should be getting enough vitamins and minerals. But even unprocessed foods are somewhat devitalized these days because of long delays between picking and eating, so I think I'll take a good all-round vitamin-mineral supplement every day as insurance.

4. *Protein*. I really think that getting enough protein with each meal helps to keep my blood sugar up and give me energy from meal to meal. So I'm going to make sure I get at each meal a high-quality protein like eggs, milk, cheese, fish, or meat. I've noticed that when I have a low-protein/high-carbohydrate lunch I tend to get a headache in the afternoon.

5. *Treats*. What do I do about my love for things like doughnuts, ice cream sundaes, pies, cakes, and candy bars? My Parent says never eat them—which is ridiculous. I know I'd eventually rebel against that—in fact, I have! My Child says eat them every day—which is equally ridiculous. So I plan to allow myself one treat a week —something I really want. It's not going to be something that's forced on me, but something I select—Dr. Bruno's assertive-eating idea. And I'm going to have it at the end of the week—like a reward, something I earn. That's a good idea—an *earned treat!*

6. *Snacks*. What do I do about snacks? Does my eating plan make allowances for them? Yes. I figure I can have two snacks a day. I usually want a snack in the afternoon—around 3 P.M.—and another snack just before I go to bed—around 10 P.M. I'm going to make sure, however, that they are either low-calorie or low-carbohydrate/high-protein snacks. If I just want to eat to eat, I'll have a low-calorie snack. If I'm actually hungry, I'll have a low-carbohydrate/high-protein snack. As Dr. Bruno suggested, I have drawn up two lists from calorie- and carbohydrate-counter booklets: one of low-calorie snacks and another of low-carbohydrate/high-protein snacks. These are all foods I like.

Here is my list of low-calorie snacks: one apple (70 calories), three or four cooked asparagus spears (25 calories), one-half cup of boysenberries (70 calories), one-half cup of cooked broccoli (60 calories), ten pieces of gumdrop candy (50 calories), two graham crackers (60 calories), two saltine crackers (30 calories), one-half cup of grapes (65 calories), six or seven canned olives (70 calories), one medium orange (65 calories), a raw green pepper (20 calories), one dill pickle (10 calories), one-half of a plain baked potato (50 calories), a tablespoon of raisins (30 calories), one-half cup of puffed rice (25 calories), a cup of beef noodle soup (70 calories), ten big fresh unsweetened strawberries (40 calories), one cup of popcorn (60 calories).

Here is my list of low-carbohydrate/high-protein snacks: one slice of gluten bread (8 grams of carbohydrate), one tablespoon of peanut butter (3 grams), one slice of American cheese (½ gram), one-half cup of cottage cheese (3 grams), one ounce of Swiss cheese (1 gram), one-half cup of plain yogurt (6 grams), one boiled egg (0 grams), a piece of broiled chicken (1 gram), four or five canned anchovies (0 grams), three fish sticks (6 grams), one-quarter can of salmon (0 grams), a medium shrimp cocktail (5 grams), one-quarter can of tuna (0 grams), a four-ounce broiled hamburger patty (0 grams), a slice of boiled ham (0 grams), three or four slices of pork bacon (2 grams), one medium frankfurter (1 gram), one slice of salami (0 grams), one-quarter cup of almonds or peanuts (7 grams).

7. *Sticking to it.* I think I can stick to this plan because it's a realistic compromise between my Parent and my Child. In the past, I've never been able to stick to a diet for very long because it was all Parent, and my Child rebelled. The diet wasn't *me.* This isn't a diet at all. As Dr. Bruno says, it's an Adult eating plan. I've really thought it through and broken the either-or barriers imposed by my Parent and my Child. For the first time I think I've hit on a way of eating that I can live with for a long time.

I might add that Diane drew up this plan more than a year ago. Following the plan, she lost twenty pounds in about fifteen weeks, a slow weight loss averaging one and one-half pounds per week. A twenty-pound loss was her goal, and she remains a normal weight. I saw her by chance three days ago. She looks good, feels good, and is able to live with the Adult eating plan, *her* eating plan—not a plan imposed by an outside authority.

ACTIVATING YOUR ADULT

In this chapter I have shown you psychological buttons you can press to activate your Adult, your wonderful biocomputer. But reading and thinking about these ideas is not enough. You have to *actually press* those buttons. If you do, you *can* lose weight, and you *can* keep it off. Here are the key ways to activate your Adult:

1. Explore effective ways of getting strokes.
2. Practice both assertive living and assertive eating.
3. Make a habitanalysis.
4. Free yourself from fat-making emotions by thinking rational thoughts.
5. Use the techniques proposed for creating psychological distance and field independence.
6. From time to time practice the exercise in which you concentrate on eating.
7. Write out dialogues between ego states.
8. Forget the Victorian concept of iron will power. Instead learn to use your skillful will to *manage* your behavior.
9. Draw up an Adult eating plan based on your knowledge of calories, carbohydrates, protein, and nutrition. Be sure that it is made by your Adult, not your Parent. If it is made by your Adult it will make realistic allowances for the demands of your Child.

And there you have it—a list of nine psychological buttons you can press to activate your Adult. The basic idea is to learn ways to apply your intelligence and free yourself from the tyranny of outdated Parent tapes, outdated Child tapes, and psychological fields that induce you to eat.

10

Freedom from Fat

Many people are slaves to food, and they remain so all their lives. Food is their master. However, this rather pathetic state of affairs need not be. Persons are not born slaves to food. They learn to overeat. In this book I have tried to show you the many routes by which people become slaves to food, and in turn the many escape routes from such slavery. If you are an overeater, and if you plug into your Adult and actually apply the ideas in this book, there is no real reason that you must continue to be at the mercy of food. The past does not have to dictate the present and the future. On the contrary, each moment we stand on the threshold of a new existence. It is helpful to focus on the saying: "Today is the first day of the rest of my life." As long as you are alive, there are new horizons.

THE PARENT PROTESTS

As you work on losing weight, you are bound to get protests from your Parent. If you are the typical person playing the role of Compulsive Eater, most of the squawking will come from your Controlling Parent. "You're not going to be able to lose weight unless you go on a strict diet." "What makes you think you're going to succeed this time when you've failed so many times before?" "Even if you lose weight you won't keep it off." "Face it—once a compulsive eater, always a compulsive eater." "Fat runs in our family." "You're fat because you have thyroid problems." "You're fat because you have defective carbohydrate metabolism." "What are you doing, leaving food on your plate! Don't you know that's wasteful?" "It isn't polite to say no to a hostess when she offers you dessert." Well, you get the idea. Your Parent will, of course, issue its own specific protests. Recognize these for what they are—outdated tapes, messages of no functional value to you if you want to change, grow, take new pathways, and lose weight. Jam the Parent tapes by activating your Adult and thinking to yourself: "You're wrong, Parent. And I refuse to listen or obey!"

CHILDHOOD'S END

It is not only the Parent that will protest. The Child will make itself heard, and its protests are of even greater consequence than those of the Parent. Again, if you are the typical person playing the role of Compulsive Eater, your Child has probably learned to demand food when it feels a stroke hunger. It has also learned to eat as a way of expressing anger. However, neither of these patterns is unalterable. They, too, are learned. Each time you obey when the Child urges you to overeat, you are making a decision. That's why I refer to Compulsive Eater as a role. It is a role you play because of psychological satisfactions associated with it. But if you become aware of these satisfactions, you can *redecide* what role you want to play in life.

You will probably have to make some compromises with the Child, working *with* your desires and impulses instead of against them. (Keep in mind the idea of the skillful will!) But you certainly do not have to be the slave of your inner Child. There is a time for childhood to end. Keep in mind this quotation from I Corinthians: "When I was a child, I spake as a child, I understood as a child, I thought as a child; but when I became a man, I put away childish things." It is time to put away childish things, those fat-making eating patterns dictated by the Child. It's time to grow up.

THE JOYS OF ADULTHOOD

You don't have to eliminate the Parent and the Child from your life when you assume the responsibilities of adulthood. An example I sometimes give is this one: You are driving to the beach. Your actual parent and your actual child are with you. Your parent says, "Watch out for that light up there! Slow down! Are you sure you're taking the right road?" Your child is jumping up and down in the back seat. "Hurry up! When are we going to get there? When we get there can I have a hot dog? Can we rent a beach umbrella? Can we go to the pier? Can we? Can we?" What do you do? Stop the car and kick them out? No, of course not. In spite of everything, the three of you are going to the beach together. *But whom do you want to remain in the driver's seat?* You, the adult, of course. Similarly, what ego state do you want to be in the driver's seat of your life? It's pretty clear that the Parent and the Child are unqualified to be in charge. You had better work on ways of placing your Adult at the wheel if you want the best for yourself in the long run.

At first it may not seem that there's much joy in adulthood. The twin attributes of adulthood—facing reality and accepting responsibility—don't sound like fun. And they're obviously difficult in and of themselves. However, facing reality and accepting responsibility are means to an end. They bring the long-term satisfactions of autonomy and intimacy. When you are autonomous you are in charge of your life, and this is a great joy. When you are capable of intimacy, you can experience the rich satisfactions of a nonmanipulative relationship. This, too, is a great joy. Indeed, autonomy and intimacy *free* the Natural Child in you to express itself. So the attainment of adulthood does not rob you of emotional expression. On the contrary!

Eating as an adult does not exclude the pleasure the Natural Child gets out of food. It *does* minimize the irrational eating demanded by the Adapted Child and the Rebellious Child, thus freeing the Natural Child to eat without guilt because it knows that its eating is under the protection of the wise Adult.

FOUR STAGES TOWARD LIBERATION

In my counseling, I have found that there are four stages through which most overeaters pass before they liberate themselves from fat. These stages are (1) denial, (2) compulsion, (3) control, and (4) spontaneity. Each person in working with his eating problem makes a kind of Pilgrim's Progress toward the ultimate goal of liberation.

Denial. Many overweight people refuse to accept the fact that they are fat. Some even dress in the dark so they don't have to see their nude bodies—ostrichlike behavior. Others deny that they have a weight problem and that they eat too much.

A state of denial is typical of those playing the roles of Slob or Fat Recluse. You will recall that Slob is associated with the I'm OK—You're not OK position. And Fat Recluse is associated with the I'm not OK—You're not OK position. These are the two most negative life positions. In Chapter Two I referred to such persons as impulsive eaters in contrast to compulsive eaters. Impulsive eaters experience very little inner struggle. This would be OK if excessive eating was not a form of self-destructive behavior. Obviously, before such individuals have any real hope of losing weight, the barrier of denial must be overcome.

Compulsion. This stage is associated with the role of Compulsive Eater. Persons in stage two are aware they are fat, and they are aware that they overeat. They are unhappy with themselves, and they want to do something about their situation. These individuals are behaving out of the I'm not OK—You're OK position, a position of hope, for they are willing to listen to advice and seek information. This is the stage of "going on a diet" and then "cheating." It is obviously a more advanced stage than the stage of denial, but there is still a great deal of emotional immaturity and self-deception. The Parent and Child are continually at war.

Those playing the role of Compulsive Eater are the ones who go to diet doctors, hypnotists, acupuncturists, psychiatrists, and psychologists. They are often the prey of unethical individuals who offer weight-control services of dubious value. The Compulsive Eater is easy prey because basically his Child is still in control, and he wishes for magic and the Wizard of Oz—the quick and easy solution to his problems and the wonderful Rescuer who can perform the fat-disappearing miracle.

In spite of all its problems, the stage of compulsion is a stage of growth. There is an inner struggle, and an awareness that something should be done. Those who continue the struggle, who do not give up and sink back into denial, often advance toward the third stage, the stage of control.

Control. The stage of control may be described as one in which the Adult is in the driver's seat. Outdated messages from the Parent and the Child are being coped with effectively. There has been a shift of internal psychological power from the Parent and the Child to the Adult. (In stage two—compulsion —the reins of psychological power are held jointly by the Parent and the Child.)

In the stage of control the skillful will and the management strategies are at work. A conscious decision is made to move toward the I'm OK—You're OK position. There is success. Weight is either being lost or being kept off. However, the stage of control requires psychological effort. It requires conscious thought, planning, and vigilance.

Spontaneity. The fourth stage—spontaneity—is the stage in which very little conscious thought has to be given to eating behavior in order to maintain a normal weight. The skillful will and the management strategies have themselves become a new set of habits. The person has finally arrived at the I'm OK—You're OK position. He often experiences a "take it or leave it" attitude toward food. At last food has been placed in its proper perspective—something needed for life, something to enjoy, but not something of inordinate importance.

Spontaneity *is* possible. But it is not a stage reached quickly or easily. Ex-overweight persons who have had their weight off for years often fluctuate between states of control and spontaneity. When they begin to lose the casual attitude toward food, they must consciously reinstate the techniques used in the stage of control. There is nothing distressing in this. There are very few things in life that run themselves without conscious thought. For example, the constant application of one's intelligence is usually required in order to run a household efficiently or to ensure the continued success of a business. Why should weight control be any different? The important thing is to have confidence in the Adult, to reach the point where one's control methods actually work.

A FINAL WORD

I sometimes think that the greatest enemy of the overeater is inertia. Thinking about, talking about, and reading about losing weight are all great. But they aren't the same as *doing it.* No weight will be lost if you don't take action.

Below is a short poem called "Mr. Meant-To" by an anonymous author. Remember it when you lose heart, incentive, or determination.

> Mr. Meant-To has a comrade,
>   And his name is Didn't-Do;
> Have you ever chanced to meet them?
>   Did they ever call on you?

These two fellows live together
In the house of Never-Win,
And I'm told that it is haunted
By the ghost of Might-Have-Been.

Don't live in the house of Never-Win. Don't be haunted by the ghost of Might-Have-Been. Take action, use your Adult, and lose weight.

Glossary

Adapted Child. That aspect of the Child ego state characterized by highly socialized behavior and an excessive effort to conform to the wishes of others.

Adult. An ego state, or domain of the personality, characterized by the ability to analyze data, think realistically, plan ahead, and take responsible action.

Anorexia nervosa. A pathological condition involving abstinence from food found mainly in teen-age girls and young women.

Antiscript. The opposite of the script; rebellion against one's script.

Antithesis. In the context of games, a "stopper," a move or set of moves that will end a particular game.

Autonomy. Self-direction; the ability to run one's own life.

Brown stamp. A bad feeling collected by the Child ego state.

Bulimia. A pathological condition involving fits of uncontrolled eating (binges).

Child. An ego state, or domain of the personality, representing the past feelings associated with one's actual childhood.

Complementary transaction. A transaction in which the response to a transactional stimulus is appropriate and expected. Represented on a TA diagram by parallel lines.

Con. In a game, an ulterior first move consisting of a social message and a psychological message.

Conditional stroke. A stroke that has to be earned.

Contamination. The encroachment of either the Parent or the Child upon the psychological territory of the Adult.

Controlling Parent. That aspect of the Parent ego state characterized by authoritarian or "bossy" behavior.

Counterscript. A script variation representing messages sent by the Parent ego states of the actual parents.

Crossed transaction. A transaction in which the response to a transactional stimulus is inappropriate and unexpected. Represented on a TA diagram by crossed lines.

Crossup. In a game, a moment of confusion on the part of the mark or patsy, immediately following the switch.

Discount. A stroke that reduces one's sense of value.

Double-bind message. A message that says "Do" and "Don't" at the same time.

Existential analysis. In the context of TA, the analysis of life positions.

Fairy godmother. In script analysis, the Nurturing Parent ego state of a mother that contributes positively toward a child's script.

Frog. A colloquialism used in TA to indicate a person suffering from chronic feelings of inferiority or low self-esteem.

Gallows transaction. An ulterior transaction in which a person elicits a smile or laughter at his misfortunes.

Game. A series of complementary ulterior transactions leading to a clear-cut, predictable, dramatic outcome.

Gimmick. In a game, a psychological weakness on the part of the respondent that can be hooked into.

Gold stamp. A good feeling collected by the Child ego state.

Hex. In script analysis, a negative injunction sent by the Child ego state of an actual parent.

Intimacy. Emotional closeness between two persons. A game-free relationship.

Jolly green giant. In script analysis, the Nurturing Parent ego state of a father that contributes positively toward a child's script.

Life position. A basic feeling about one's inferiority or superiority in relationship to the same traits in others. The life position is adopted in early childhood.

Life style. According to the depth psychologist Alfred Adler, a characteristic way of coping with the world.

Little Professor. The intuitive dimension of the Child ego state, which enables the young child to perceive body talk, facial gestures, tone of voice, and other such cues as a kind of communication.

Natural Child. That aspect of the Child ego state characterized by the capacity for joy, play, and spontaneous action.

Negative stroke. An unpleasant experience that provides some partial satisfaction of one's recognition hunger.

Nurturing Parent. That aspect of the Parent ego state characterized by the capacity to give unconditional positive strokes to other persons.

Ogre father. In script analysis, the Child ego state of a father who hexes a child with a negative injunction.

Parent. An ego state, or domain of the personality, representing the influences during childhood of actual parents and other authority figures.

Payoff. In a game, the collection of either good feelings (gold stamps) or bad feelings (brown stamps).

Permissive Parent. As formulated in this book, that aspect of the Parent ego state characterized by the allowance of impulsive and/or irresponsible behavior.

Positive stroke. A pleasant experience that provides some partial satisfaction of one's recognition hunger.

Prince or Princess. A colloquialism used in TA to suggest the natural state of human beings—a state characterized by feelings of competence and high self-esteem.

Psychological distance. A self-induced feeling that one is subjectively remote from a stimulus (e.g., food) that is objectively nearby.

Psychological level. In a transaction, the level of a message that is ulterior or hidden from view.

Racket. A self-indulgent pattern of behavior involving dishonest dealings in either bad feelings (brown stamps) or good feelings (gold stamps).

Rebellious Child. That aspect of the Child ego state characterized by undersocialized behavior and an excessive tendency to behave in impulsive and irresponsible ways.

Recognition hunger. The need to be noticed, attended to, and loved.

Role. In a game, a social pose adopted to attain ulterior ends.

Script. An unconscious life plan adopted in childhood or early adolescence.

Script protocol. A rough draft of the script, a preliminary image of what life will be like when one grows up.

Shooting script. The final version of the script, complete with a cast of stock characters.

Skillful will. As formulated by Roberto Assagioli, the ability to use one's will to obtain desired results in practical and effective ways.

Social level. In a transaction, the level of a message that is apparent or held forth to view.

Stimulus hunger. The need for sensory experiences—to see things, to hear sounds, to touch objects, to smell various fragrances, and to taste foods.

Stimulus-induced eating. Eating that takes place in response to certain invitational characteristics associated with food, not to an inner state of actual hunger.

Stroke. An experience that satisfies recognition hunger. Strokes can be either positive or negative.

Structural analysis. The analysis of the personality in terms of the Parent, the Adult, and the Child ego states.

Structure hunger. The need to structure time with some kind of purposeful activity.

Switch. In a game, the surprise move with which the instigator of the game turns the tables on the mark.

Trading stamp. A feeling collected by the Child ego state.

Transaction. The unit of social action, involving a stimulus and a response.

Transactional Analysis. As formulated by Eric Berne, a systematic study of the human communication process.

Ulterior transaction. A transaction in which more than two ego states are active at the same time. Ulterior transactions have two levels—social and psychological.

Unconditional stroke. A stroke that is given spontaneously without ulterior aims.

Witch mother. In script analysis, the Child ego state of a mother that hexes a child with a negative injunction.

Wooden leg. From Berne's game of the same name, a weak, self-indulgent excuse for a particular behavior.

Bibliography

Assagioli, Roberto. *The Act of Will.* New York: Viking Press, 1973.

Bach, Richard. *Jonathan Livingston Seagull.* New York: Macmillan, 1970.

Berne, Eric. *Games People Play.* New York: Grove Press, 1964. Paperback: Grove Press, 1967.

————. *Principles of Group Treatment.* New York: Oxford University Press, 1966. Paperback: Grove Press, 1968.

————. *Transactional Analysis in Psychotherapy.* (Paperback) New York: Grove Press, 1961. Also, Ballantine, 1975.

————. *What Do You Say After You Say Hello?* New York: Grove Press, 1972. Paperback: Bantam, 1973.

Buber, Martin. *I and Thou.* New York: Scribner, 1958.

Galbraith, John K. *The Affluent Society.* Boston: Houghton Mifflin, 3rd ed., 1976. Paperback: New American Library, 1959.

Ginott, Haim G. *Between Parent & Child.* New York: Macmillan, 1965. Paperback: Avon, 1973.

Gordon, Thomas. *P.E.T. Parent Effectiveness Training.* New York: Peter H. Wyden, 1970. Paperback: New American Library, 1975.

Harris, Thomas A. *I'm OK—You're OK.* New York: Harper & Row, 1967. Paperback: Avon, 1976.

O'Connor, Richard. *Jack London.* Boston: Little, Brown, 1964.

Schachter, Stanley, and Rodin, Judith. *Obese Humans and Rats.* Potomac, Md.: Lawrence Erlbaum Associates, Publishers, 1974.

Steiner, Claude M. *Scripts People Live.* New York: Grove Press, 1974. Paperback: Bantam, 1975.

Stevens, John O. *Awareness: Exploring, Experimenting, Experiencing.* (Paperback) Moab, Utah: Real People Press, 1971. Also, Bantam, 1973.

Zimbardo, Philip G. *Shyness: What It Is, What to Do About It.* Reading, Mass.: Addison-Wesley, 1977.

Index

Action, 155–156
Act of Will, The (Assagioli), 174–175
Acupuncture, 46
Adapted Child, 33–35, 40–42, 50,
    79–81, 85, 89–90, 94, 112, 182
Additives, food, 168–169
Adler, Alfred, 77, 138
Adult-Adult transactions, 110
Adult eating plan, 175–177
Adult ego state, 6, 17, 20, 27–30,
    48–51, 90, 94–98, 154–178. *See
    also* Games; Scripts
  action, 155–156
  activating, 178
  assertiveness, 159–162
  defined, 11–12
  eating, concentration on, 171–172
  ego states, dialogues between,
      172–173
  emotional slavery, freedom from,
      164–166
  habits, 162–163
  insight, 155–156
  psychological distance and field
      independence, 167–170
  skillful will concept, 174–175, 183,
      184
  strokes and. *See* Strokes
Advertising. *See* Food industry
Affectional drive, 34
Affluent Society, The (Galbraith), 70

"Alice in Fatland," 131–132
Alienation, 88, 90, 91
Anger, 164
Animistic thinking, 59
Anorexia nervosa, 150–151
Anthropomorphic thinking, 59
Antiscript, 149, 150–151
Antisocial reaction, 87
Antithesis, 135
Anxiety, 164
Anyone Got a Match? (Shulman),
    168–169
Assagioli, Roberto, 174–175
Assertive eating, 161–162, 175
Assertive living, 159–161, 164
Attribution, 15
Authoritarian parent, 14–15
Autonomy, 8–9, 136–137, 181
Awareness, 43
Awareness (Stevens), 136

Balanced meals, 23–24
Behavior modification techniques,
    130–131, 156
Berne, Eric, 4, 9, 11, 18, 46, 75,
    101, 117, 135
Between Parent & Child (Ginott), 17
Binges, 27, 50, 89, 90
Blood glucose, 4
Blood sugar, 24, 25
Breakfast, 25

Breakfast cereals, 69–70
Brown stamps, 39–40, 107
Buber, Martin, 82
Buck, Pearl S., 12
Bulimia, 90

Calories, 175–177
Carbohydrates, 3, 42, 69, 176, 177
Cereals, 69–70
Child-Child transactions, 103–104,
    110–112
Child ego state, 6, 12, 31–51,
    164–166, 180–181. *See also*
    Games; Scripts
  Adapted Child, 33–35, 40–42, 50,
    79–81, 85, 89–90, 94, 112, 182
  composition of, 33–37
  contacting, 47–48
  coping with, 48–51
  defined, 11–12
  ego states, dialogues between,
    172–173
  excuses, 43–45
  food industry and. *See* Food
    industry
  friends and, 40–42
  kid foods and, 42–43
  Little Professor, 33, 37–38
  magic and, 45–47, 55
  Natural Child, 33, 36–37, 80–81,
    85–86, 89–90, 95–96, 182
  rackets, 39–40, 108
  Rebellious Child, 33, 36, 80,
    84–86, 88–90, 94, 182
  trading stamps, 38–40
Child-Parent transactions, 105–106,
    112
Cleaning plate, 20
Coffee shops, 60–62
Complementary transactions,
    101–106
Compulsion, 182–183
"Compulsive Eater" ("Someone to
    Watch Over Me"), 119–122
Compulsive eating, 16–17, 32, 37,
    182

Con
  "Compulsive Eater," 120
  defined, 117
  "Fat Clown," 126
  "Fat Recluse," 123
  "Help Me Lose Weight, Dr.
    Dodo," 129
  "If You Loved Me for Me," 125
  "Look How Hard I've Tried to
    Lose Weight," 127
Conditional strokes, 35
"Conquest of Fat Mountain" script,
    143–144
Contamination, 81, 96, 172
Control, 183, 184
Controlling Parent, 17–18, 31, 40,
    68, 79, 81, 88, 89, 94, 179–180
Counterscript, 149–150
Covert cues, 162
Critical Parent, 27, 91, 94
Crossed transactions, 106–108
Crossup
  "Compulsive Eater," 121
  defined, 117–118
  "Fat Clown," 126–127
  "Fat Recluse," 124
  "Help Me Lose Weight, Dr.
    Dodo," 130
  "If You Loved Me for Me," 125
  "Look How Hard I've Tried to
    Lose Weight," 128
Curie, Marie, 12
Curses, 139–141

Democratic parent, 17
Denial, 182
Depression, 159, 160, 164
Dessert, 62, 65, 176
Diabetes, 143
Diet, 26–27
Discounts, 100–101, 107
Disraeli, Benjamin, 153
Double-bind messages, 54, 146–147
"Dumbo," 133
Duplex message, 14

Eating. *See* Meals
Ego, 12
Ego states. *See* Adult ego state;
  Child ego state; Parent ego
  state
Einstein, Albert, 12
Eliot, T. S., 143
Emotional slavery, freedom from,
  164–166
"Everybody Look at Me," 144–146
Excuses, 43–45
Existential analysis, 6–7

Fairy godmothers, 140
Fake strokes, 80, 84
"Fat Clown" ("Watch Me Make a
  Fool of Myself"), 126–127
"Fat Recluse" ("I Never Go
  Anywhere"), 122–124
Feeling talk, 160, 164
Field independence, 167–170
Fogging, 160–161
Food additives, 168–169
Food industry, 52–73
  better restaurants, 64–65
  breakfast cereals, 69–70
  coffee shops, 60–62
  magazine promotion, 53–57
  supermarkets, 65–68
  take-out chains, 62–64
  television advertising, 57–60
Food-related cues, 49, 52–53, 72,
  162, 166, 170
Freedom, 16, 145
Freud, Sigmund, 11, 155
Friendship, Child ego state and,
  40–42
Frog, 9

Galbraith, John Kenneth, 70
Gallows transactions, 111–113
Games, 117–137, 139
  "Compulsive Eater," 119–122
  defined, 8
  elements of, 117–118
  ending, 135–136
  "Fat Clown," 126–127

"Fat Recluse," 122–124
game-free living, 136–137
"Help Me Lose Weight, Dr.
  Dodo," 129–131
"If You Loved Me for Me,"
  124–125
"Look How Hard I've Tried to
  Lose Weight," 127–128
players, 118
reasons for playing, 119
wooden legs, 131–135
Games People Play (Berne), 75, 101
Gestalt therapy, 31
Gimmick
  "Compulsive Eater," 120–121
  defined, 117
  "Fat Clown," 126
  "Fat Recluse," 123–124
  "Help Me Lose Weight, Dr.
    Dodo," 129
  "If You Loved Me for Me," 125
  "Look How Hard I've Tried to
    Lose Weight," 127–128
Ginott, Haim, 17
"Going Crazy" script, 146–148
Gold stamps, 39–40
Gordon, Thomas, 17, 115
Gourmet, role of, 132

Habitanalysis, 162–163, 175
Habits, 162–163
Harlow, Harry, 34
Harris, Thomas, 11
"Help Me Lose Weight, Dr. Dodo,"
  129–131
Henley, William Ernest, 92–93
Hexes, 139–142, 145, 146
"Hollow Men, The," (Eliot), 143
Hunger, kinds of, 4–6
Hyperactivity, 148
Hyperemotionability, 148
Hypoglycemia, 143

Id, 12
"If You Loved Me for Me," 124–125
I-it relationship, 82
I-messages, 115–116, 165

I'm not OK—You're not OK life
    position, 76, 87–91, 97
I'm not OK—You're OK life
    position, 2, 74–82, 96
I'm OK—You're not OK life
    position, 76, 82–87, 96
I'm OK—You're OK (Harris), 11
I'm OK—You're OK life position, 7,
    76, 91–98
Implied consent, 62
Impulsive eating, 16, 32–33, 37, 182
Impulsive purchases, 66–68
Inferiority complex, 77
Insight, 155–156
Interpersonal theory of
    psychopathology, 99–100
Intimacy, 8–9, 136–137, 181
"Invictus" (Henley), 92–93, 170
I-thou relationship, 82

Jonathan Livingston Seagull (Bach),
    136
Jolly green giants, 140
"Junk Food Junkie," 134–135

Kid foods, 42–43

Learning theory, 156
License, 16, 145
Life positions, 6–7, 74–98. *See also*
    Games; Scripts
  I'm not OK—You're not OK, 76,
    87–91, 97
  I'm not OK—You're OK, 2, 74–82,
    96
  I'm OK—You're not OK, 76,
    82–87, 96
  I'm OK—You're OK, 7, 76, 91–98
Life style, 138
Little Professor, 33, 37–38
London, Jack, 78–79
"Look How Hard I've Tried to Lose
    Weight," 127–128
"Looking for love" script, 141–143
Low-calorie snacks, 176–177
Low-carbohydrate/high-protein
    snacks, 177

Magazine promotion, 53–57
Magic, Child ego state and, 45–47,
    55
Management strategies, 175, 183,
    184
Meals
  balanced, 23–24
  breakfast, 25
  cleaning plate, 20
  concentration on eating, 171–172
  eating between, 21–23
  skipping, 24–25
  three square meals, concept of, 19
  wasting food, 20–21, 161
Meat eating, 85
"Mr. Meant-To," 184–185
"My Destiny," 133–134

Natural Child, 33, 36–37, 80–81,
    85–86, 89–90, 95–96, 182
Negative strokes, 5–6
Neurotic reactions, 81
Normal weight, 9
Nurturing Parent, 17–18, 56–57, 79,
    84, 88, 94

Obsessive-compulsive reaction, 81
O'Connor, Richard, 78
Ogre fathers, 141, 142, 145, 146,
    149, 152
Overeating, defined, 3–4

Parent-Child transactions, 104–105,
    108–109
Parent Effectiveness Training
    (Gordon), 17
Parent ego state, 2, 6, 10–30. *See
    also* Games; Scripts
  balanced meals, 23–24
  breakfast eating, 25
  cleaning plate, 20
  composition of, 17–18
  contacting, 27–28
  Controlling Parent, 17–18, 31, 40,
    68, 79, 81, 88, 89, 94, 179–180
  coping with, 28–30

Parent ego state *(continued)*
Critical Parent, 27, 91, 94
eating between meals, 21–23
ego states, dialogues between,
172–173
Nurturing Parent, 17–18, 56–57,
79, 84, 88, 94
Permissive Parent, 15–18, 83, 86
skipping meals, 24–25
three square meals concept, 19
wasting food, 20–21, 161
Parent-Parent transactions, 102–103,
109–110
Parents, 13
kinds of, 14–17
Pavlov, Ivan, 156
Payoff
"Compulsive Eater," 121
defined, 118
"Fat Clown," 127
"Fat Recluse," 124
"Help Me Lose Weight, Dr.
Dodo," 130
"If You Loved Me for Me," 125
"Look How Hard I've Tried to
Lose Weight," 128
Perls, Frederick ("Fritz"), 31
Permissive Parent, 15–18, 83, 86
Personality disorder, 87
Piaget, Jean, 59
Positive strokes, 5–6
Preservatives, 169
Primates, 34
Prince or princess, 9, 140
Protein, 42, 43, 66–67, 69, 176
Psychological distance, 167–170,
175
Psychological field, 166–170
Psychological level, 108–110
Psychosis, 91
Psychotic depression, 148
Psychotic reactions, 90, 147

Rackets, 39–40, 108
Rebellious Child, 33, 36, 80, 84–86,
88–90, 94, 182

Recognition hunger, 5–6
Restaurants, better, 64–65
Roles, 118
Roosevelt, Eleanor, 12, 115
Russell, Bertrand, 12

School of Nutrition and Public
Health, Loma Linda, California,
24–25
Schweitzer, Albert, 12
Scripts, 138–153
antiscript, 149, 150–151
breaking free from, 151–153
"Conquest of Fat Mountain,"
143–144
counterscript, 149–150
defined, 8–9
"Everybody Look at Me,"
144–146
"Going Crazy," 146–148
hexes and curses, 139–141
"Looking for Love," 141–143
protocol, 141
shooting script, 141
Self-fulfilling prophecy, 2, 15
Self-stroking, 49, 50
Sensory focusing, 171–172
Shooting script, 141
Shulman, Max, 168–169
Shyness, 157–158
*Shyness: What It Is, What to Do
About It* (Zimbardo), 158
Sisyphus, myth of, 143, 144
Skillful will, 174–175, 183, 184
Skinner, B. F., 156
Skipping meals, 24–25
Snack eating, 21–23, 176–177
Social level, 108–110
Sociopaths, 87
Spitz, René, 34
Spontaneity, 183–184
Spontaneous eating, 37
Stevens, John O., 136
Stimulus hunger, 4–5
Stimulus-induced eating, 49, 52–53,
72, 162, 166

Stroke hunger, 34, 35, 38, 80, 84, 94, 156, 157
Strokes, 5–6, 34–35, 100–101. *See also* Games
  conditional, 35
  fake, 80, 84
  negative, 5–6
  positive, 5–6
  self-, 49, 50
  unconditional, 157
  ways of getting, 156–159
Structural analysis, 6
Structure hunger, 5, 119
Suicide, 146, 148
Sullivan, Harry Stack, 99
Superego, 11
Supermarkets, 65–68
Switch
  "Compulsive Eater," 121
  defined, 117
  "Fat Clown," 126
  "Fat Recluse," 124
  "Help Me Lose Weight, Dr. Dodo," 129–130
  "If You Loved Me for Me," 125
  "Look How Hard I've Tried to Lose Weight," 128

Take-out chains, 62–64
Television advertising, 57–60
Three square meals, concept of, 19
Top dog, 31
Trading stamps, 38–40

Transactional analysis
  defined, 1
  overview of, 6–9
  truth and, 2–3
Transactions, 99–116
  complementary, 101–106
  crossed, 106–108
  freedom from fat-making, 114–116
  gallows, 111–113
  ulterior, 108–111, 135

Ulterior transactions, 108–111, 135
Unconditional strokes, 157
Underdog, 31

Vitamins, 176

Wasting food, 20–21, 161
Watson, John B., 156
Weight, normal, 9
What Do You Say After You Say Hello? (Berne), 33
"Why Don't You–Yes But," 127
Will power, 174
Witch mothers, 141, 142, 145, 146, 149, 152
Wooden legs, 44, 131–135

X-raying the food, 168, 171

Zimbardo, Philip G., 158